1969

# Les choses

# Georges Perec

# LES CHOSES

a story of the sixties

Translated by Helen R. Lane

Grove Press, Inc., New York

# Les choses

To Denis Buffard

*Incalculable are the benefits civilization has brought us, incommensurable the productive power of all classes of riches originated by the inventions and discoveries of science. Inconceivable the marvelous creations of the human sex in order to make men more happy, more free, and more perfect. Without parallel the crystalline and fecund fountains of the new life which still remains closed to the thirsty lips of the people who follow in their griping and bestial tasks.*

—MALCOLM LOWRY

# Part One

THE EYE, AT FIRST, would glide over the gray rug of a long corridor, high and narrow. The walls would be cabinets, whose copper fittings would gleam. Three engravings—one representing Thunderbird, the winner at Epsom, another a paddle-wheel steamer, the "Ville-de-Montereau," the third a Stephenson locomotive—would lead to a leather curtain, hanging from large rings of black-veined wood, that a simple gesture would suffice to slide back. The rug, then, would give way to an almost yellow parquet floor, which three rugs in soft colors would partially cover.

It would be a living room, about twenty-one feet long and nine feet wide. On the left, in a sort of alcove, a large couch of worn black leather would be flanked by two bookcases in pale wild-cherry wood, on which books would be piled helter-skelter. Above the divan a nautical chart would run the whole length of the wall panel. Beyond a little low table, under a silk prayer rug attached to the wall with three copper nails with large heads, and balancing the leather hanging, another divan, perpendicular to the first, upholstered in light brown velvet, would lead to a small piece of furniture on high legs, lacquered in dark red, with three shelves that would hold bric-a-brac: agates and stone eggs, snuffboxes, jade ashtrays, a mother-of-pearl shell, a silver pocket watch, a cut-glass tumbler, a crystal pyramid, a miniature in an oval frame. Farther on, past a padded door, corner shelves, one atop the other, would contain small boxes and records, next to a closed phonograph of which only four machine-turned steel knobs would be visible, and above it an engraving representing "The Grand Procession of the Festival of the Carrousel." From the window, hung with black and brown imitation *toile de Jouy* curtains, a few trees, a tiny park, a bit of the street could be seen. A roll-top desk, crammed with papers and pen boxes, would have next to it a little cane-bottomed armchair. A console table would hold a telephone, a leather datebook, a pad of paper. Then, past another door, after a pivoting bookshelf, low and square, with a large cylindrical vase decorated in blue and filled with yellow roses on top of it, and above it an oblong mirror set in a mahogany frame, a narrow table, with two benches upholstered in Scotch plaid, would lead back to the leather curtain.

Everything would be brown, ocher, tawny, yellow: a universe of somewhat faded colors, in tones carefully, almost preciously set against each other, and the few brighter touches among them would come as a surprise: the almost gaudy orange of a cushion, a few bright-colored book jackets tucked among the leather bindings. In broad daylight the light flooding the room would make it seem a bit sad, despite the roses. It would be an evening room. Then in winter, with the curtains drawn, with a few spots of light—the corner with the bookshelves, the record collection, the desk, the low table between the two couches, the vague reflections in the mirror—and the great zones of shadow where everything would gleam—the polished wood, the heavy rich silk, the cut crystal, the supple leather—it would be a haven of peace, the land of happiness.

The first door would open onto a bedroom, with a light-colored rug covering the floor. A large English-style bed would fill one end of the room. On the right, on each side of the window, two high narrow shelves would contain favorite books frequently read, albums, decks of cards, jars, necklaces, knickknacks. On the left, an old oak wardrobe and two wooden and copper clothes trees would face a little low chair upholstered in gray silk with a fine stripe, and a dressing table. A half-open door, leading to a bath-room, would disclose thick dressing gowns, copper swan's-neck faucets, a large adjustable mirror, a pair of English razors and their green leather cases, bottles, brushes with horn handles, sponges. The walls of the room would be hung in chintz; the bed would be covered with a Scotch plaid blanket. A night table, edged on three sides with a metal band of pierced copper, would hold a silver candle-stick lampbase with a very pale gray lampshade, a little quadrangular clock, a rose in a footed glass, and, on its lower shelf, folded newspapers, a few magazines. Farther on, at the foot of the bed, there would be a large ottoman of natural leather. At the windows, voile curtains would slide on copper curtain rings; the double drapes, in thick gray wool, would be half drawn. The room would still be bright in the half-light. On the wall, above the bed turned down for the night, between two little lamps from Alsace, the astonishing long, narrow, black and white photograph of a bird high in the sky would come as a surprise because of its somewhat formal perfection.

The second door would disclose a study. The walls would be covered from top to bottom with books and magazines, with here and there, to break the succession of bindings and spines, a few engravings, drawings, photo-graphs—the "Saint Jerome" of Antonello da Messina, a detail from "The Triumph of Saint George," a prison by Piranesi, a portrait by Ingres, a little pen-and-ink landscape by Klee, a sepia photograph of Renan in his study at the Collège de France, a department store by Steinberg, the portrait of Melanchthon by Cranach—hung on panels of wood set into the bookshelves. A little to the left of the window and at a slight angle, there would be a long Lorraine table covered with a red blotter. Wooden containers, long pen cases, jars of all sorts would contain pencils, paperclips, metal clips, staples. A glass brick would serve as an ashtray. A round box in black leather, decorated with arabesques in fine gold, would be filled with cigarettes. The light would come from an old desk lamp, difficult to adjust, with a shade of green opal glass in the shape of an eyeshade. On each side of the table, almost facing each other, there would be two leather-and-wood armchairs with high backs. Still farther to the left, along the wall, there would be a narrow table piled with books. A club chair of bottle-green leather would lead to gray metal filing cabinets, to index-card boxes in light wood. A third table, still smaller, would hold a Swedish lamp and a typewriter with an oilcloth cover. At the very end of the room there would be a narrow bed, covered in imported velvet, with cushions in all different colors. A tripod of painted wood, almost in the center of the room, would hold a map of the world in German silver and papier-mâché, naïvely illustrated, a fake antique. Behind the desk, half masked by the red curtain at the window, a waxed wooden stepladder would be able to glide along a copper track that would go all the way around the room.

Life there would be easy, would be simple. All the obligations, all the problems that practical life implies, would easily be overcome there. A cleaning woman would come every morning. Every two weeks, wine, oil, sugar would be delivered. There would be a huge sunny kitchen, with blue tiles in a heraldic pattern, three porcelain plates decorated with yellow arabesques with metallic reflections, shelves everywhere, a handsome table of white wood in the center of the room, stools, benches. It would be pleasant to come sit there every morning after a shower, not yet dressed for the day. On the table would be a large stone butter dish, jars of marmalade, honey, toast, grapefruit cut in half. It would be early. It would be the beginning of a long day in May.

They would open their mail, unfold the newspapers. They would light a first cigarette. They would go out. Their work would take them only a few hours in the morning. They would meet again for lunch, for a sandwich or a mixed grill, whichever they preferred; they would have coffee at a sidewalk café, then take a leisurely stroll back home.

Their apartment would rarely be in order, but its very disorder would be its greatest charm. They would pay little attention to it; they would live with it. The comfort surrounding them would seem an accomplished fact, a given premise, a state of their nature. Their attention would turn elsewhere: to the book they would open, to the text they would write, to the record they would listen to, to talking together, as they did each day anew. They would work a long time, without panic or hurry, without feelings of bitterness. Then they would have dinner, or go out to dinner; they would meet their friends; they would take a walk together.

It sometimes seemed to them that a whole life could go harmoniously by between these book-lined walls, among these objects so perfectly domesticated that the two of them would end up believing that they had been forever created for their own use alone, among these beautiful, simple, mellow, luminous things. But they would not feel themselves tied down by them; on certain days they would go looking for adventure. Nothing they planned would be impossible. Rancor, bitterness, envy would be foreign to them. For their means and their desires would match in every detail, at all times. They would call this balance happiness, and through their freedom, through their wisdom, through their cultivated tastes they would know how to preserve it, how to discover it at each instant of their lives in common.

THEY WOULD HAVE LIKED TO BE RICH. They thought they would have known how to be. They would have known how to dress, how to look, how to smile like rich people. They would have had the necessary tact, the necessary discretion. They would have forgotten their wealth, they would have known how not to make a show of it. They would not have boasted about it. They would have breathed it. Their pleasures would have been intense. They would have liked to walk, to stroll, to choose, to appreciate. They would have enjoyed living. Their life would have been an art of living.

These things are not easy; quite the contrary. For this young couple, who were not rich, but who wanted to be simply because they were not poor, there could not have been any more uncomfortable a situation. They had only what they deserved to have. While they dreamed of space, of light, of silence, they were thrown back on the reality (not even a threatening one, but simply a narrowed one— and that was perhaps worse) of their tiny living quarters, their daily meals, their skimpy vacations. It was what went with their economic situation, their social position. It was their reality, and they had no other. But there existed alongside them, all around them, all along the streets they couldn't help but walk in, the deceptive yet heartwarming displays of antique dealers, grocers, stationers. From the Palais Royal to Saint-Germain, from the Champ-de-Mars to the Étoile, from the Luxembourg to Montparnasse, from the Ile Saint-Louis to the Marais, from Ternes to the Opéra, from the Madeleine to the Parc Monceau, Paris was a perpetual temptation. They yearned to succumb to it, drunkenly, immediately, eternally. But the horizon of their desires was pitilessly blocked; their great impossible dreams were nothing but a utopia.

They lived in a tiny, charming, low-ceilinged apartment which looked out on a garden. Remembering the maid's room that they had lived in—a dark, narrow, overheated passageway with clinging odors—they lived in the apartment at first in a sort of drunkenness, renewed each morning by the chirping of the birds. They would open the windows and look at their courtyard for long minutes at a time, perfectly happy. The building was old, not yet falling apart, but run down and full of cracks. The passageways and stairways were narrow and dirty, sweating with dampness, impregnated with greasy smoke. But between two great trees and five tiny gardens (irregular in shape, growing wild for the most part, but full of grass hard to come by, of flowers in pots, of bushes, and even of naïve statues), there wound a path of large, irregular paving stones, which gave the whole scene a country air. It was one of those rare spots in Paris where on certain autumn days after a rain an aroma might rise from the ground, an almost overpowering aroma of forest, of humus, of rotting leaves.

They never tired of these charms, and still remained as spontaneously conscious of them as they had been at first, but it became evident, after a few months of over-carefree joy, that these charms would not be enough to make them forget the drawbacks of their living quarters. Accustomed to living in unhealthy rooms where all they did was sleep, spending their days in some café, it took them a long time to realize that the most banal activities of everyday life—sleeping, eating, reading, chatting, washing—each required a specific space, the notorious absence of which then began to be noticeable. They consoled themselves as best they could, congratulating themselves on how excellent the neighborhood was, how close the rue Mouffetard and the Jardin des Plantes were, how quiet the street was, what cachet their low ceilings had, how splendid the trees and the courtyard were all through the year. But inside the apartment everything was beginning to be one big jumble of objects: furniture, books, dishes, papers, empty bottles. An exhausting war was beginning, which they were never to win.

With a total area of forty square yards, which they never dared to measure exactly, their apartment consisted of a minuscule entry, a tiny kitchen, one half of which had been turned into a bathroom, a bedroom of modest dimensions, an all-purpose room—library, living room or workroom, guest room—and an ill-defined corner, halfway between a miscellaneous closet and a corridor, where they managed to squeeze in a small-sized refrigerator, an electric water heater, a makeshift clothes closet, a table on which they ate their meals, and a chest for dirty clothes that they also used for a bench.

Sometimes the lack of space became tyrannical. They were smothering to death. But they tried in vain to push back the limits of their two rooms, to tear down walls, to fashion corridors, shelves, passageways, to imagine model closets, to annex neighboring apartments in their dreams. They always ended up finding themselves once again in what was their lot, their only lot: forty square yards.

Sensible arrangements would doubtless have been possible: a partition could have been taken down, freeing a large corner that wasn't of much use, a piece of furniture that was too large could have been replaced to good advantage, a row of shelves could have been built in. If only it could have been repainted, scoured, arranged with a little love, their apartment would doubtless have been really charming, with its window with red curtains and its window with green curtains; with its long, somewhat wobbly oak table, bought at the Flea Market, which occupied the whole length of one wall panel, beneath the very handsome reproduction of an old nautical chart, the panel that a little Second Empire roll-top desk, in mahogany inlaid with copper fillets, several of which were missing, separated into two work spaces, one for Sylvie on the left, one for Jérôme on the right, each of them provided with the same red blotter, the same glass brick, the same jar of pencils; with its old glass jar with a pewter edge that had been turned into a lamp, with its ten-liter grain measure in veneer reinforced with metal which served as a wastebasket, with its two unmatched armchairs, its rush-bottomed chairs, its milking stool. Neat and clean, ingenious, the apartment as a whole would have given the impression of a friendly warmth, a pleasant atmosphere of work being done, of lives being shared.

But the very thought of the work to be done frightened them. They would have had to borrow, save, invest money. They couldn't resign themselves to it. Their heart was not in it: they thought only in terms of everything or nothing. Either the library would be of light oak or there would be no library. There was no library. Books piled up on two shelves of dirty wood, and on two shelves in cupboards which should never have been used for books. An electric outlet was defective for three years without their ever making up their minds to have an electrician in, and meanwhile wires with crude splices and awkward extensions ran along almost all the walls. It took them six months to replace a curtain pull. And the slightest neglect of daily housekeeping tasks within twenty-four hours brought about a disorder that the beneficent presence of trees and gardens so near at hand made more unbearable still.

The provisional, the status quo, reigned as absolute masters. They no longer looked forward to anything but a miracle. They would somehow summon architects, contractors, masons, plumbers, upholsterers, painters. They would go on a cruise and come back to find an apartment that was transformed, all neatly arranged, made new, a model apartment, miraculously enlarged, full of things made to order: movable partitions, sliding doors, an efficient and noiseless heating system, invisible electric wiring, good furniture.

But no rational plan for reconciling objective necessities and their financial possibilities ever came to fill the gap between these overgrandiose dreams, to which they abandoned themselves with a strange complacency, and the fact that they were getting nothing done. The immensity of their desires paralyzed them.

This absence of single-mindedness, of clear thinking almost, was characteristic. They felt a cruel lack of ease—it was doubtless this that was the most serious. Not material, objective ease, but a certain lack of constraint, a certain lack of tension. They had a tendency to be excited, tense, avid, jealous almost. Their love of comfort, of comfort plus, most often expressed itself in a silly search for fellow disciples. They and their friends would then babble on about the special charm of a pipe or a low table; they would turn them into art objects, museum pieces. They would get all enthused about a suitcase—those tiny, unusually flat valises in fine-grained black leather which can be seen in the windows of shops around the Madeleine, and which seem to concentrate in themselves all the supposed pleasures of lightning-quick trips to New York or London. They would go from one end of Paris to the other to see an armchair that someone had said was perfect. And, knowing their classics, they even hesitated sometimes to put on a new article of clothing; it needed to be worn three times before it would look just right. But the somewhat hieratic gestures they made when they got all enthused in front of the window of a tailor or a milliner or a shoemaker usually managed only to make them look a bit ridiculous.

Perhaps they (and not only they, but also their friends, their colleagues, people their age, the world in which they moved) were too marked by their past. Perhaps they were too voracious from the outset; they wanted to go too fast. It would have been necessary that the world, things, belong to them from the beginning; they would then have marked these things with multiple signs that they possessed them. But they were condemned to acquisition: they could become richer and richer; they could not make it true that they had always been rich. They would have liked to live in comfort, amid beauty. But they exclaimed, they admired; this was the surest proof that they hadn't arrived there yet. They lacked tradition—in the most despicable sense of the word, perhaps: self-evident truth, genuine enjoyment, implicit and immanent, that enjoyment which is accompanied by a well-being of the body, whereas their pleasure was all cerebral. In what they called luxury they too often liked only the money that had gone into it. They succumbed to the signs of wealth; they loved wealth before they loved life.

Their first excursions outside the world of students, their first forays into this universe of luxury department stores that was soon to become their Promised Land, were particularly revealing from this point of view. Their still-uncertain taste, their qualms, their lack of experience, their somewhat blind respect for what they thought were the norms of true good taste, caused them a few humiliations, a few false notes. It might for a moment have seemed that the sartorial model that guided Jérôme and his friends was not the English gentleman but the quite continental caricature of him offered by a recent emigrant on a modest salary. And the day that Jérôme bought his first British shoes, he was careful—after having rubbed them for a long time, pressing delicately in little concentric motions with a wool rag and a bit of polish of a superior quality—to expose them to sunlight, which was supposed to cause them to acquire an exceptional shine immediately. Except for a pair of heavy moccasins with crepe soles, which he stubbornly refused to wear, it was, alas, the only pair of shoes he owned. He took bad care of them, scuffed them on rough ground, and ruined them in a little less than seven months.

Then, with the help of age and the experiences they had had, they seemed to be able to hold out a bit better against their most fervent desires. They learned how to wait, and how to live with them. Their taste gradually grew more confident, more discriminating. Their desires had time to ripen; their greed became less nagging. When they stopped in at village antique shops as they strolled on the outskirts of Paris, they no longer pounced on porcelain plates, church chairs, blown-glass demijohns, copper candlesticks. In the somewhat static image they had of the model house, of perfect comfort, of the happy life, there was, certainly, still a great deal of naïveté, a great deal of complacency. They passionately loved those objects that only the taste of the moment considered handsome: fake Épinal prints, English-style engravings, agates, spun-glass tumblers, neo-barbarian knickknacks, para-scientific bric-a-brac, which in no time they discovered again in all the shop windows of the rue Jacob, the rue Visconti. They still dreamed of possessing them; they could thus have gratified the immediate, evident need to be up on things, to be considered connoisseurs. But this excessive desire to imitate grew less and less important, and they liked to think that they had rid their image of life of all trace of what had been overeager, flashy, childish at times. They had burned what they had adored: convex ornamental mirrors, chopping blocks, stupid little mobiles, radiometers, multicolored pebbles, burlap panels with scribbles in the style of Mathieu. It seemed to them that they were more and more masters of their desires: they knew what they wanted; they had clear ideas. They knew what their happiness, their freedom, would be like.

And yet they were wrong: they were losing their way. Already they were beginning to feel that they were being dragged down a road, knowing neither where it led nor where it ended. They were afraid sometimes. But most often they were only impatient. They felt ready, they were free; they were waiting to live, they were waiting for money.

JÉRÔME WAS TWENTY-FOUR; SYLVIE WAS TWENTY-TWO. They were both psycho-sociologists. Their work, which was not exactly a trade, nor yet a profession, consisted of interviewing people, by various techniques, on a number of subjects. It was difficult work that demanded, at the very least, a high degree of concentration, but it did not lack interest, paid relatively well, and left them considerable free time.

Like almost all their colleagues, Jérôme and Sylvie had become psycho-sociologists out of necessity, not out of choice. Heaven knows where the free development of their completely idle inclinations would have led them. History, here again, had chosen for them. Like everyone else, they would have liked, certainly, to dedicate themselves to something, to feel in themselves a powerful need that they would have called a vocation, an ambition that would have uplifted them, a passion that would have fulfilled them. Alas, they recognized in themselves only one passion: to live better, and that one exhausted them. As students, the prospect of getting a mere intermediate degree, a post at Nogent-sur-Seine, Château-Thierry, or Étampes, and a small salary, horrified them so much that very soon after they met (Jérôme was then twenty-one and Sylvie nineteen), almost without the need of talking it over together, they gave up studies that they had never really begun. The desire to know did not consume them. Much more

25

humbly, and without concealing from themselves the fact that doubtless they were wrong, and that sooner or later there would come a day when they would regret it, they felt the need of a little larger room, running water, a shower, meals that would be more varied, or simply more ample, than those at the university restaurants, a car perhaps, records, vacations, clothes.

Motivation studies had made their appearance in France several years before. That year they were still in a period of rapid expansion. New agencies were coming into being every month, starting from scratch, or almost. It was easy to find work in them. It consisted, most of the time, of going into public gardens as school was letting out, or into low-cost housing projects in the suburbs, and asking housewives whether they had noticed some recent advertisement and what they thought of it. These rapid-fire surveys, called testings or minute-interviews, paid one hundred francs each. It was not very much, but it was better than baby-sitting, than being a night watchman, than dishwashing, than all the measly jobs—distributing brochures, timing radio advertisements, doing accounting, selling door to door, tutoring—that were traditionally set aside for students. And then the very newness of the agencies, their almost artisan-like status, the novelty of their methods, the total lack still of qualified personnel, allowed room for the hope of rapid promotion, dizzying climbs up the ladder.

It was not a bad chance to take. They spent several months interviewing. Then there happened to be a director of an agency who was pressed for time and took a chance on them. They left for the provinces, a tape-recorder under their arm. Some of their traveling companions, hardly much older than they were, initiated them into the techniques of open and closed interviewing, which are really less difficult than is generally supposed. They learned how to make other people talk, and to measure their own words; they learned to spy out, beneath vague hesitations, beneath confused silences, beneath timid allusions, the paths that should be explored; they caught on to the secrets of the universal "hmmm," a veritable magic intonation, which the interviewer uses to punctuate the words of the interviewee, to give him confidence, understand him, encourage him, question him, and even sometimes threaten him.

Their results were commendable. They were off to a good start, and kept on. They picked up, here and there, bits of sociology, psychology, statistics; they assimilated the vocabulary and the symbols, the tricks that made a good impression—a certain way, for Sylvie, of putting on or taking off her glasses, a certain way of taking notes, of leafing through a report, a certain way of talking, of inserting in their conversations with their bosses, in a slightly interrogative tone of voice, phrases such as: "isn't that right?" . . . "I think perhaps" . . . "it's a question I'm asking," a certain way of quoting, at opportune moments, C. Wright Mills, William Whyte, or better still, Lazarsfeld, Cantril, or Herbert Hyman, of whose works they had not read three pages.

They showed excellent talents for picking up these absolutely necessary acquisitions that were the ABC of their work, and barely a year after their first contact with motivation studies they were given the heavy responsibility of making a "contact analysis": a job just below that of general director of a study, necessarily restricted to executives who sat in an office—the highest, and hence the most coveted, the most highly esteemed post in the whole hierarchy. In the course of the years that followed, they hardly ever descended from these heights.

And for four years, perhaps more, they explored, interviewed, analyzed. Why do tank-type vacuum cleaners sell so badly? What opinion do people in modest circumstances have of chicory? Is prepared purée liked, and why? Because it's light? Because it's rich? Because it's so easy to make— just one thing to do, and there you are? Do baby carriages really seem too expensive? Aren't people always ready to make a sacrifice for the sake of their children's comfort? How will the French woman vote? Do people like cheese in tubes? Are people for or against public transportation? What do people eating yoghurt first notice? The color? The consistency? The taste? The natural flavor? Do you read a great deal, a little, not at all? Do you go to restaurants? Madame, would you like renting a room to a Negro? What's your frank opinion of pensions for old people? What do young people think? What do executives think? What do thirty-year-old women think? What do you think of vacations? Where do you spend your vacations? Do you like frozen foods? How much do you think a lighter like this costs? What qualities do you require your mattress to have? Can you describe to me a man who likes noodles, spaghetti, and macaroni? What do you think of your washing machine? Are you satisfied with it? Doesn't it make too many suds? Does it wash well? Does it tear clothes? Does it dry clothes? Would you prefer a washing machine that would dry your clothes too? Is mine safety adequate, or isn't there enough, in your opinion? (Make the subject talk; ask him to recount personal examples, things that he's seen. Has he already been hurt himself? How did it happen? And will his son be a miner like his father? If not, what?)

There was clothes-washing, clothes-drying, ironing. Gas, electricity, telephone. Children. Clothes and underclothes. Mustard. Packaged soup powders, canned soup. Hair— how to wash it, how to dye it, how to make it hold a wave, how to make it shine. Students, fingernails, cough syrups, typewriters, fertilizers, tractors, leisure-time activities, gifts, stationery, linen, politics, highways, alcoholic drinks, mineral waters, cheeses and jam, lamps and curtains, insurance, gardening.

Nothing human was alien to them.

They earned some money for the first time. They did not like their work: could they have liked it? On the other hand, they were not too bored by it either. They had the impression they were learning a great deal from it. Year by year it changed them.

These were the great hours of their conquest. They had nothing; they were discovering the world's richnesses.

They had long been perfectly anonymous. They dressed like students, that is to say, badly, Sylvie in a single skirt, ugly sweaters, a pair of velvet pants, a duffel coat, Jérôme in a dirty fur-lined jacket, a ready-made suit, a lamentable tie. They plunged delightedly into English fashion. They discovered wools, silk blouses, Doucet shirts, voile ties, silk scarves, tweed, lambswool, cashmere, vicuña, leather and jersey, linen, the magistral hierarchy of shoes, finally, that leads from Churches to Westons, from Westons to Buntings, and from Buntings to Lobbs.

Their dream was a trip to London. They would have divided up their time between the National Gallery, Savile Row, and a certain pub on Church Street that Jérôme had fond memories of. But they were not yet rich enough to

29

dress themselves from head to foot in London. In Paris, with the first money joyfully earned by the sweat of their brow, Sylvie purchased a knitted silk blouse at Cornuel's, an imported lambswool twin-sweater set, a severe straight skirt, extremely soft braided-leather shoes, and a large silk square decorated with peacocks and leaves. Though Jérôme still liked on occasion to lounge around in old shoes, unshaven, dressed in collarless old shirts and drill pants, he discovered, with an eye out for contrasts, the pleasures of long, lazy mornings: bathing, shaving closely, splashing himself with toilet water, and with his skin still slightly damp, putting on an impeccably white shirt, knotting a tie of silk or wool. He bought three of them at Old England, and also a tweed jacket, some shirts that were on sale, and shoes he felt he didn't have to be ashamed of.

Then—and it was almost one of the red-letter days in their lives—they discovered the Flea Market. They found marvelous Arrow or Van Heusen shirts with long button-down collars (impossible to come by in Paris at that time, although they were beginning to be popular because of American comedies—at least among that restricted fringe of people who find their happiness in American comedies), piled up there in a big heap, alongside supposedly inde-structible trench coats, skirts, blouses, silk dresses, leather jackets, soft leather moccasins. They went there every other week on Saturday mornings for a year or more, to dig around in the boxes, the stalls, the piles, the cartons, the umbrellas turned upside down, amid a crowd of teen-agers with spit curls, Algerian watch sellers, American tourists who had emerged from the glass eyes, the top hats, and the wooden horses of the Vernaison market and were wandering about, somewhat terrified, in the Malik market, contemplating, alongside the old nails, mattresses, carcasses of machines, and spare parts, the strange destiny of the tired surpluses of their most prestigious shirtmakers. And they brought back clothes of all sorts, wrapped in newspapers; and knickknacks, umbrellas, old jars, leather knapsacks, records.

They were changing, becoming different. It was not so much the need (and it was a real need) to be different from the people it was their job to interview, to impress them without dazzling them. Nor was it because they were meeting lots of people, because they were leaving—forever, it seemed to them—the circles they had once belonged to. But money brought new needs. (Such a remark is necessarily banal.) If they had thought about it for a moment (but in those years they didn't think), they would have been surprised to notice how much change there had been in their view of their own bodies, and beyond that, in their view of everything that concerned them, everything that mattered to them, everything that was becoming their world.

Everything was new. Their sensibilities, their tastes, their position: everything was taking them toward things they had never known. They paid attention to how other people were dressed; they noticed furniture, knickknacks, ties in store windows; they dreamed in front of real estate agents' advertisements. It seemed to them that they understood things they had never bothered about before: it had become important to them whether a neighborhood, a street, was sad or gay, quiet or noisy, deserted or lively. Nothing, ever, had prepared them for these new preoccupations; they discovered them ingenuously, enthusiastically, marveling at their long ignorance. They were not surprised, not very often anyway, that they thought about them almost all the time.

The paths they followed, the values they embraced, their views, their desires, their ambitions: all these things, it is true, sometimes seemed desperately empty to them. They were acquainted with nothing that was not fragile or confused. Yet it was their life; it was the source of strange, more than intoxicating, elations; it was something immensely, intensely open. They sometimes said to themselves that the life they would lead would have the charm, the flexibility, the fantasy of American comedies, of Saul Bass film titles; and marvelous, luminous images of immaculate fields of snow streaked with ski tracks, of blue sea, of sun, of green hills, of fires crackling in stone fireplaces, of high-speed highways, of pullmans, of palaces, touched them lightly, like so many promises.

They gave up their room and university restaurants. They found a place for rent at number 7, rue de Quatrefages, opposite the Mosque, right near the Jardin des Plantes: a little two-room apartment overlooking a pretty garden. They felt a sudden desire to have rugs, tables, armchairs, divans.

They took interminable walks around Paris in these years. They stopped in front of every antique dealer's. They visited department stores, for hours on end, amazed and terrified without yet daring to say so, without yet daring to face up to this sort of pitiful, ravening greed that was to become their destiny, their reason for being, their slogan, amazed and already almost submerged by the vastness of their needs, by the wealth spread out before them, by the abundance offered.

They discovered little restaurants around Gobelins, Ternes, Saint-Sulpice, deserted bars where it was fun to whisper together, weekends outside Paris, long walks in the forest in autumn, at Rambouillet, at Vaux, at Compiègne, the almost perfect joys offered everywhere to the eye, to the ear, to the palate.

Thus, little by little, coming into a little deeper contact with reality than they had had in the past when, as children of narrow-minded petits bourgeois and then as amorphous students just like all the other students, they had only a limited and superficial vision of the world, they now began to understand what a gentleman was. This last revelation—which was, moreover, not a revelation in the strict sense of the term, but rather the end product of a long social and psychological maturation whose successive stages they would have been hard put to describe—crowned their metamorphosis.

LIFE WITH THEIR FRIENDS WAS OFTEN A WHIRLWIND.
They were a group unto themselves, a fine team.
They knew each other well; rubbing off on each other, they
had common habits, tastes, memories. They had their own
vocabulary, their own symbols, their own hobbies. Too
mature to resemble each other perfectly, but doubtless not
yet mature enough not to imitate each other more or less
consciously, they spent a great deal of their life sharing
things with each other. It often irritated them; more often
it amused them.

They belonged, almost all of them, to advertising circles.
Some of them, however, were continuing, or trying to
continue, some vague sort of studies. They had usually
met each other in the offices of heads of agencies. They
listened together, fiercely scribbling their petty recom-
mendations and their sardonic jokes in their notebooks.
Their common scorn for these fat cats, these profiteers,
these soup merchants was sometimes their first meeting
ground. But usually they first felt condemned to living
five or six days together in the dreary hotels of small towns.
With every meal eaten together they invited friendship to
sit down with them. But lunches were hasty and business-
like, and dinners frightfully long-drawn-out, unless that
remarkable spark was struck that lighted up their mourn-
ful traveling-salesman faces and made them find this evening in the provinces memorable, and the nondescript potted meat (that a rascally hotel owner charged extra for)

very tasty. At such times they forgot all about their tape-recorders and dropped their overcareful, distinguished-psychologist tone of voice. They lingered at the table. They talked of themselves and the world, of everything and nothing, of their tastes, of their ambitions. They scoured the town looking for the only comfortable bar, which must surely exist somewhere, and with their whiskies, brandies, or gin-and-tonics in front of them, they would speak with an almost ritual abandon of their loves, their desires, their travels, their rebellions, their enthusiasms, without ever being surprised—on the contrary, they were almost delighted—at how similar their life stories were, how identical their views were.

It sometimes happened that nothing resulted from these first feelings of friendship except vaguely keeping in touch by telephone from time to time. It also happened—less frequently, it is true—that from this first meeting there would develop, by chance or by desire on the part of both, slowly or not so slowly, a possible friendship that little by little became more intimate. Thus, as the years went by, they would slowly grow closer and closer.

They were all easily identifiable. They had money, not too much, but enough so that they were forced into deficit financing only occasionally, following some spending spree that was either a luxury or a necessity, though they could not have said which it was. Their apartments, studios, attics, two-room apartments in run-down houses in choice neighborhoods—the Palais Royal, the Contrescarpe, Saint-Germain, the Luxembourg, Montparnasse—all looked alike: they all had the same grimy couches, the same so-called rustic tables, the same piles of books and records, the same old pots, old bottles, old tumblers, old glass jars full of either flowers, pencils, change, cigarettes, candy, or paperclips. They all dressed more or less in the same way, that is to say, with that adequate taste, for men and women alike, that makes "Madame Express" and the spouse who echoes her such valuable guides. They owed a great deal to this model couple.

*L'Express* was undoubtedly the weekly they paid most attention to. They didn't like it very much, to tell the truth, but they bought it, or in any case borrowed it from each other; they read it regularly and even frequently saved back numbers of it (they admitted as much). Far more often than not they happened not to agree with its political views (one day they wrote, in healthy anger, a short pamphlet on "the Lieutenant's style"), and they much preferred the analyses in *Le Monde,* to which they were unanimously faithful, or even the stands taken by *Libération,* with which they tended to find themselves in agreement. But *L'Express,* and it alone, corresponded to their way of life; each week they found in it the commonest preoccupations of their everyday life, even though they might rightfully judge them to be travestied and distorted. It was not a rare thing for them to be shocked by it. For really, in the face of this style where false distance, innuendo, hidden scorn, simmering envy, false enthusiasms, footsie-playing, suggestive winks, reigned; in the face of this advertising circus that *L'Express* represented—its end and not its means, its most necessary aspect; in the face of these little details that change everything, these really amusing little trifles; in the face of these businessmen who understood the real problems, these technicians who knew what they were talking about and let you know it, these bold thinkers who, pipe in their mouth, gave birth to the twentieth century; in the face, in a word, of this assemblage of responsible men, meeting together each week in a forum or a round-table discussion, whose beatific smile gave the impression that they held in their right hand the golden keys to the executive washroom, they imagined, no doubt about it, repeating the not very good pun that opened their pamphlet, that it was not certain that *L'Express* was a *leftist* weekly, but that it was beyond all doubt a *sinister* weekly. They knew very well, moreover, that this was false, but it comforted them.

They faced up to it: they were *L'Express*'s kind of people. They doubtless needed to have their freedom, their intelligence, their gaiety, their youth, in all times, in all places, properly pointed out somewhere. They let *L'Express* take them in hand, because it was the easiest thing to do, because the very scorn they felt for it justified them. And the violence of their reactions was equaled only by their submissiveness; they leafed through it, grumbling the while, wadded it into a ball, threw it away. There was sometimes no end to how they carried on about its infamy. But the fact was, they read it; they saturated themselves with it.

Where could they have found a truer reflection of their tastes, their desires? Were they not moderately rich? *L'Express* offered them all the signs of well-being: thick dressing gowns, brilliant exposés, beaches that were "in," exotic cuisine, useful shortcuts, intelligent analyses, the secret of the gods, little inexpensive holes in the wall, different views, new ideas, little dresses, frozen foods, elegant details, polite scandal, last-minute advice.

They dreamed, in a half-whisper, of Chesterfield divans. *L'Express* dreamed with them. They spent a large part of their vacations running down country sales; they bought bargains in pewter, straw-bottomed chairs, glasses that fairly invited one to drink, knives with horn handles, bowls with a patina that made darling ashtrays. They were sure of all these things: *L'Express* had talked about them, or was about to.

As far as buying was concerned, however, they departed significantly from the ways of going about it that *L'Express* recommended. They had not yet "settled down" completely, and although they were quite willingly given the status of "executives," they had neither the guarantees, nor the year-end bonuses, nor the fringe benefits of regular personnel working under contract. *L'Express* therefore recommended "inexpensive, friendly little boutiques" (the manager is a pal; he offers you a drink and a club sandwich while you make your choice), out-of-the-way places where the taste of the day demanded, as a proper setting, a radical improvement of what had been there before. Whitewashed walls were indispensable; a *bouclé* rug was a necessity, and only an old-looking, irregular mosaic-tile floor could pretend to replace it; exposed beams were *de rigueur;* and a little interior stairway, a real fireplace with a fire, and rustic or, better still, provincial furniture were highly recommended. These transformations were taking place all over Paris, affecting alike bookstores, galleries, notion shops, knickknack and furniture shops, and even grocery stores (it was not unusual to see a former retail merchant down on his luck become Mr. Cheeseman, with a blue apron that gave him the look of a connoisseur and a shop with beams and straw on the floor). These same transformations brought about, more or less legitimately, a rise in prices such that it constantly proved impossible to buy a hand-printed natural-wool dress, a cashmere twin-sweater set woven by a blind peasant woman in the Orkney

Islands (exclusive, genuine, vegetable-dyed, hand-spun, hand-woven), or a splendid jacket, half worsted and half leather (for the weekend, for hunting, for the car). And just as they ogled in antique shops but actually bought their furniture only at country sales or in the less-frequented exhibition rooms of the Hôtel Drouot (where they went, moreover, less frequently than they would have liked to), so all of them expanded their wardrobe only by assiduously frequenting the Flea Market or, twice a year, the bazaars organized by aged English ladies for the benefit of the charitable endeavors of St. George's English Church, where there abounded cast-off clothing of diplomats, which naturally was quite acceptable. They often felt a bit embarrassed: they had to make their way through a dense crowd and rummage about through a pile of horrors—the English do not always have the taste people say they have—before coming up with a superb tie, doubtless too frivolous for an embassy secretary, or a shirt that had once been perfect, or a skirt in need of shortening. But of course it was that or nothing: the disproportion, everywhere visible, between the quality of their taste in clothes (nothing was too good for them) and the quantity of money they ordinarily had available was an obvious, but in the end a secondary, sign of their actual situation; and they were not the only ones. Rather than buy such bargains as were offered everywhere three times a year, they preferred to buy second-hand. In the world that was theirs, it was practically a rule always to desire more than one could acquire. It was not they who had so decreed; it was a law of civilization, a given fact of which advertisements in general, magazines, the art of display, the spectacle of the streets, and even, in a certain way, the whole of those productions commonly called cultural, were the

truest expression. They were wrong, consequently, to feel
at certain times that their dignity had been violated. These
slight mortifications—asking the price of something in an
uncertain tone of voice, hesitating, trying to bargain,
ogling show windows without daring to go in, coveting,
looking shabby—also made the wheels of commerce go
round. They were proud of having paid a cheaper price
for something, of having gotten something for nothing, or
almost nothing. They were prouder still (but one always
pays a little bit dearly for the pleasure of paying too
dearly) of having paid a great deal, the most possible, on
the spot, without haggling, almost drunkenly, for what
was, what could not but be, the handsomest, the uniquely
handsome, the perfect. These feelings of embarrassment
and of pride had the same function, brought the same dis-
appointments, the same nagging doubts. And because
everywhere, all around them, everything forced them to
understand, because it was dinned into their heads all day
long, what with slogans, posters, neon signs, lighted windows, they understood that they were always a little lower
on the ladder, always just a little too low. Still, they were
lucky not to be the worst off of all; far from it.

They were "a new breed," young executives who had
not yet cut all their teeth, technocrats halfway along the
road to success. They came, almost all of them, from the
petite bourgeoisie, and its values, they thought, were no
longer good enough for them. They looked, with envy,
with despair, toward the obvious comforts, the luxury, the
perfection of the grands bourgeois. They had no past, no
tradition. They expected no inheritance. Among all of
Jérôme's and Sylvie's friends, only one came from a rich
and well-established family: drygoods merchants from the

North, a tidy and solid fortune, real estate in Lille, titles, a gentleman's estate near Beauvais, goldwork, jewels, whole rooms of furniture centuries old. For all the rest of their friends, childhood had been lived against a background of dining rooms and bedrooms furnished in Chippendale or Norman provincial style, as these were beginning to be conceived in the dawn of the 30's: beds in the middle of the room, covered with flaming red taffeta, wardrobes with three doors, decorated with mirrors and gilt, frightfully square tables with turned legs, coatracks with fake deer antlers. In the evening, beneath the one lamp for the whole family, they had done their homework. They had put out the garbage, gone for the milk, gone out slamming the door behind them. Their childhood memories were all alike, since the paths they had followed, their slow emergence from the family circle, the prospects they seemed to have chosen for themselves, were almost identical.

They thus belonged to their times. They felt they had themselves well in hand. They were not complete dupes, they would say. They knew how to keep their distance. They were relaxed, or at least tried to be. They had a sense of humor. They were far from being stupid.

An exhaustive analysis would easily have turned up, in the group that they formed, divergent currents, veiled antagonisms. A scrupulous, careful sociometric researcher would soon have discovered cleavages, mutual exclusions, latent hostilities. It sometimes happened that one or another of them, after more or less fortuitous incidents, half-hidden provocations, half-veiled misunderstandings, would sow discord among the group. Then their fine friendships would dissolve. They would discover, with feigned amazement, that so-and-so, whom they believed to be generous, was really the soul of niggardliness, that somebody else was just plain selfish. Conflicts arose; there were rifts. They sometimes took a malicious pleasure in marshaling forces against each other. Or else there were periods when they sulked too long, when they were markedly distant and cold to each other. They avoided each other and endlessly justified themselves for it, until the hour struck for pardons, for letting bygones be bygones, for warm reconciliations, because when all was said and done they could not get along without each other.

Such games kept them very busy, and they spent precious time on them that they might very well have employed for something completely different. But they were so constituted that however irritated they might be by it from time to time, the group that they formed was still almost their only definition of themselves. They had no real life of their own outside of it. They were wise enough, however, not to see each other too often, not to work together all the time. They even tried to keep some activities all to themselves, private zones where they could escape, where they could for a time forget, not the group itself, the Mafia, the team, but the work that kept the group going. Their almost communal life made studies, departures for the provinces, nights of writing analyses or reports easier; but it also condemned them to such activities. It was, one may venture to say, their secret drama, their common weakness. It was what they never talked about, ever.

Their greatest pleasure was to forget together, that is to say, to have a good time. They adored drinking, first of all, and they often drank a great deal together. They frequented Harry's New York Bar, rue Daunou, the cafés of the Palais Royal, the Balzar, Lipp's, and a few others. They liked Munich beer, Guinness, gin, hot or iced punches, fruit brandies. They sometimes devoted whole evenings to drinking, crowded around two tables placed together for the occasion, and they talked endlessly of the life they would have liked to lead, the books that they would write someday, the work they would like to undertake, the films they had seen or were going to see, the future of mankind, the political situation, their coming vacations, their past vacations, an outing in the country, a little trip to Bruges, to Antwerp, or to Basel. And sometimes, plunging deeper and deeper into these collective dreams, making no effort to wake up from them, but rather tossing them out endlessly with a tacit complicity, they would end up losing all contact with reality. Then from time to time a hand would emerge from the group, the waiter would come, take away the empty steins and bring others, and soon the conversation, bogging down more and more, would touch only on what they had just had to drink, on how drunk they were, how thirsty they were, how happy they were.

On these nights they were in love with freedom. It seemed to them that the whole world was made to their measure; they were attuned to the exact rhythm of their thirst, and their exuberance was unquenchable, their enthusiasm knew no bounds. They could have walked, run, danced, sung all night long.

They did not see each other the next day. Couples stayed shut up at home, not eating, nauseated, drinking too much coffee and taking too many effervescent tablets. They would come out only when night had fallen, and go off to eat a plain steak at an expensive snack-bar. They made harsh decisions: they wouldn't smoke any more, wouldn't drink any more, wouldn't waste money any more. They felt empty and foolish, and into the memory they had of their unforgettable drinking bout there always crept a certain nostalgia, a vague nervous exhaustion, an ambiguous feeling, as if the very thing that had led them to drink had merely revived a more fundamental lack of understanding, a more insistent feeling of irritation, a more stubborn contradiction, which they could not get out of their minds.

Or else they organized dinners that were almost gargantuan, really gala parties at the home of one or another of the group. Most of them had only tiny kitchens that sometimes were impossible to move around in, and unmatched dishes with here and there a few rather impressive pieces. On the table, exquisite cut-crystal glasses were set next to glasses that mustard had come in, and kitchen knives next to emblazoned silver teaspoons.

They would all come back together from the rue Mouffetard, their arms loaded with groceries, with whole hampers of melons and peaches, baskets full of cheeses, legs of lamb, poultry, baskets of oysters in season, terrines, roe, and whole cases, finally, of wine, port, mineral water, Coca-Cola.

There were nine or ten of them. They would fill the small apartment, where all the light came from a single window opening onto the courtyard. A couch covered in coarse velours occupied the back of an alcove; three people would sit on it facing the table when dinner was ready; the others would find places on unmatched chairs or on stools. They would eat and drink for hours. The exuberance and the abundance of these meals were curious. To tell the truth, they were mediocre from a strictly culinary point of view: the roasts and poultry had no sauces to go with them; the vegetables almost invariably were sautéed or boiled potatoes; at the end of the month there were even noodles or rice with olives and a few anchovies as the main dish. They made no sort of experiments; their most complex preparations were melon with port, bananas in flaming brandy, cucumbers with sour cream. It took them several years to realize that there was a technique, if not an art, of cooking, and that everything that they had especially loved to eat was nothing but raw material, with no frills and no subtlety.

In this they gave evidence, once again, of their ambiguous situation: their idea of a festive meal corresponded, detail for detail, to the meals that for a long time were the only sort they had ever had, those of the university restaurants. Because they had eaten so much thin, tough beef-steak, they made a veritable cult of chateaubriands and filets. Meats with sauces did not appeal to them, and for a long time they were even suspicious of stews, having all too vivid a memory of pieces of fat swimming around among three slices of carrot, in the intimate company of a squashed cream cheese and a spoonful of rubbery jam. Somehow they liked everything that had nothing to do with the kitchen and everything to do with showy display. They liked abundance and richness to be obvious; they rejected the slow preparation that transforms unpromising products into food for the table and implies a universe of frying pans, casseroles, chopping knives, rotary graters, stoves. But the sight of a delicatessen sometimes made them almost faint, because everything there is immediately edible: they liked pâtés, mixed-vegetable salads decorated

with garlands of mayonnaise, ham rolls, and eggs in aspic;
they succumbed to them too often, and regretted it, once
their eyes had been satisfied, once their fork had cut into
the aspic garnished with a slice of tomato and two pieces of
parsley, for it was, after all, only a hard-boiled egg.

Above all, there were movies. And this was doubtless the
only area in which their sensibilities had taught them
everything. Here they owed nothing to models. They belonged, because of their age and their upbringing, to that
first generation for whom cinema was more a fact of life
than an art: they had always known it, and not as a stam-
mering art form, but from the very first as a form with
its masterpieces, its mythology. It sometimes seemed to
them that they had grown up with it, and that they understood it better than anyone else before them ever had.

They were movie fans. Films were their first love; they
were so addicted to them that they went every night, or
almost every night. They liked images, so long as they were
beautiful, so long as they captivated them, delighted them,
fascinated them. They liked the conquest of space, time,
movement; they liked the whirlwind pace of the streets of
New York, the torpor of the tropics, the violence of
saloons. They were neither too sectarian, like those dull
sorts who swear by one man—Eisenstein, Buñuel, or
Antonioni, or else (it takes all kinds to make a world)
Carné, Vidor, Aldrich, or Hitchcock—nor too eclectic, like
those infantile individuals who lose all their critical faculties if only a blue sky looks sky blue, or the bright red of
Cyd Charisse's dress stands out against the dark red of
Robert Taylor's divan. They were not without taste. They
had a strong prejudice against so-called serious cinema,
which made them find the movies that were not rendered

47

a waste of time by this adjective more beautiful still. (But all the same, they said, what a crashing bore *Marienbad* was, and they were right.) They had an almost extravagant fondness for westerns, thrillers, American comedies, and for astonishing adventures blown up with lyric flights of fancy, sumptuous images, striking and almost inexplicable flashes of beauty, such as *The Bad and the Beautiful, Written on the Wind, The Crimson Pirate,* and they always remembered them.

They seldom went to concerts, and even less frequently to the theater. But they bumped into each other at the Cinémathèque, the Passy, the Napoléon, or at little neighborhood movie houses—the Kursaal at Gobelins, the Texas in Montparnasse, the Bikini, the Mexico on the Place de Clichy, the Alcazar at Belleville, and others too, out toward the Bastille or the fifteenth arrondissement. They were badly equipped theaters with no charm, which seemed to be frequented only by a mixed audience of men out of work, Algerians, bachelors, and movie hounds. But they showed (in disgraceful dubbed versions) those unknown masterpieces which they had remembered ever since they were fifteen, or those films (they kept a list of them in their heads) that they had heard were works of genius and had been trying to see for years. They remembered with amazement those hallowed evenings when they had discovered, or rediscovered, almost by chance, *The World in His Arms, Night on the City, High Wind in Jamaica.*

It is true, alas, that they were often cruelly disappointed. These films that they had waited so long to see, leafing almost feverishly through *L'Officiel des Spectacles* each Wednesday the minute it came out, these films that all sorts of people had assured them were admirable, sometimes happened at last to be showing somewhere. They found the house full the first night. The screen would light up, and they would shiver with joy. But the colors were dated, the film was jerky, the women had aged terribly. They left; they felt sad. It was not the film they had dreamed of. It was not that total film that each of them bore within himself, that perfect film that they would never have enough of, the film that they would have liked to make. Or, doubtless more secretly, that they would have liked to live.

So THEY LIVED, they and their friends, in their crowded and charming little apartments, with their outings and their films, their huge fraternal meals, their marvelous plans. They were not unhappy. Certain furtive, evanescent joys of living brightened their days. On certain evenings, after they had finished dinner, they would be reluctant to get up from the table; they would finish off a bottle of wine, nibble on nuts, light cigarettes. On certain nights, they could not get to sleep, and propped up against the pillows, an ashtray between them, they would talk till morning. On certain days, they would walk and talk for hours. They would look at each other in store windows and smile. It seemed to them that everything was perfect; they walked along with abandon; their movements were relaxed; time seemed no longer to touch them. Just being there in the street, warmly dressed on a cold, dry, blustery day at nightfall, walking without hurrying but at a good quick pace toward a friend's place, was enough to make their slightest gesture—lighting a cigarette, buying a cone of hot chestnuts, threading their way through the crowd at a railroad station exit—seem to them like the evident, immediate expression of a boundless happiness.

Or else, on certain summer nights, they would take long walks in sections of the city they hardly knew at all. A perfectly round moon would be shining high in the sky and casting a velvety light on everything. The streets—long,

deserted, broad, echoing—would resound with their foot-
falls as they walked along in step with each other. At rare
intervals taxis would pass by slowly, almost noiselessly.
At such times they felt like masters of the world. They felt
an unknown excitement, as if they were possessed of fabu-
lous secrets, inexpressible powers. Taking each other by
the hand, they would begin to run, or play hopscotch, or
hop along the sidewalks, singing the great arias from
*Così fan tutte* or the *B-Minor Mass* together.

Or else they would push open the door of a little restaurant and with an almost ritual joy allow themselves to
be penetrated by the warmth of the place, the click of
forks, the clinking of glasses, the soft sound of voices, the
promises of the white napkins. They would choose their
wine gravely, unfolding their napkins, and at that moment
it would seem to them, in the cozy warmth with just the
two of them together, smoking a cigarette that they would
put out, an instant after they had begun it, when the
hors d'oeuvre arrived, that their life would be but the
inexhaustible sum of these propitious moments and that
they would always be happy because they deserved to be,
because they knew how to stay free, because happiness was
within them. They would be sitting across from each
other, they would be about to eat after having been
hungry, and all these things—the coarse white linen table-
cloth, the touch of blue of a package of Gitanes, the porcelain plates, the somewhat heavy silverware, the footed
glasses, the wicker basket full of fresh bread—composed
the frame, never twice the same, of an almost visceral
pleasure, bordering on numbness: the impression—almost
exactly contrary to and almost exactly the same as that pro-
duced by speed—of a marvelous stability, a marvelous

plenitude. Beginning with this table all set up, they had the impression of a perfect state of synchronization: they were in unison with the world, they bathed in it, they were at ease in it, they had nothing to fear from it.

Perhaps they knew, a little bit better than other people, how to decipher, or even to call forth, these favorable signs. Their ears, their fingers, their palates, as if they were constantly on the alert, waited only for these propitious instants, which a mere nothing sufficed to set off. But in these moments when they let themselves be carried away by a feeling of flat calm, of eternity, which no tension came to disturb, where everything was in balance, deliciously slow, the very strength of these joys heightened everything that was ephemeral and fragile in them. It did not take much to make the whole thing fall to pieces: the slightest false note, a simple moment of hesitation, a sign just a bit too crude, and their happy mood disintegrated. It became what it had never ceased to be, a sort of contract, something they had bought, something fragile and pitiful, a simple instant of respite that sent them violently back to what was most dangerous, most uncertain in their existence, in their history.

The trouble with interviews is that they don't last. The day when they would have to choose was already written in Jérôme's and Sylvie's history: either be out of work or employed part time, or else put down more solid roots in an agency, work in it full time, become an executive in it, or get into some other kind of work, find a job somewhere else, except that this would merely postpone the problem. For if it is quite permissible for individuals who haven't yet reached the age of thirty to preserve a certain independence and to work only when they feel like it, and even if their freedom, their open minds, the variety of their experience, or what is still referred to as their many-sidedness is appreciated, it is nonetheless required, on the other hand (and moreover, quite contradictorily), that a future employee, once past the thirty-year mark (thus making—and rightly—the age of thirty the cut-off point), give proof of a certain stability, some guarantee of punctuality, seriousness, loyalty, discipline. Employers, particularly in advertising, not only refuse to take on employees past thirty-five but also hesitate to put their confidence in someone who at thirty has never been "permanently employed." As for continuing to use such people only on a part-time basis, as if nothing had changed, even that is impossible: instability makes it look as if you weren't serious; at the age of thirty you owed it to yourself to have gotten someplace, or else you don't amount to anything. And nobody has gotten anywhere if he hasn't found his place, hasn't dug in, hasn't got his keys, his desk, his little name plate.

Jérôme and Sylvie often thought about this problem. They still had a few years to go, but the life they were leading, the relative peace they enjoyed, would never be secure. Everything would go to pieces; they would have nothing left. They did not feel overburdened by their work, they were sure of making a living, more or less, year in, year out, somehow or other, without work consuming their whole lives. But that was not to last.

One never remains a mere interviewer very long. As soon as he is broken in, a psycho-sociologist climbs to the higher echelons as fast as he can. He becomes assistant director or director of an agency, or finds a much-coveted job as head of a department in some large agency, in charge of recruiting personnel, training programs, public relations, marketing policy. These are fine jobs: the offices have rugs on the floor, two telephones, a Dictaphone, a built-in refrigerator, and sometimes even a painting by Bernard Buffet on one of the walls.

Alas, Jérôme and Sylvie often thought and sometimes said aloud to each other: work not, eat not, of course, but people who work don't live. They thought they had had that experience once for a few weeks. Sylvie had gotten a job as an office clerk in a research outfit; Jérôme coded and decoded interviews. Their working conditions were more than pleasant: they came to work whenever they felt like it, read the paper in the office, made frequent trips downstairs to have a beer or a cup of coffee. They even felt a certain liking for the work they were so dilatory about doing, encouraged by the very vague promise of a steady job, a formal contract, rapid promotion. But they didn't last long. They would wake up in the morning in a frightfully irritable mood; they would come home on crowded subways at night full of resentment; they would fall onto the divan, dirty and dead tired, and dream only of long weekends, days with nothing to do, and sleeping all morning.

They felt as if they were in a prison, caught like rats in a trap. They couldn't resign themselves to it. They still thought that a great many things could happen to them, that the very regularity of their hours and the same routine day after day, week after week, were drawbacks they did not hesitate to call hellish. It was in any case the beginning of a fine career. A fine future lay before them; they had arrived at those epic moments when the boss sums you up as a young man, congratulates himself *in petto* for having taken you on, is anxious to train you, to fashion you in his own image, invites you to dinner, thumps you on the belly, and with a single gesture opens the gates of fortune for you.

They were stupid—how many times they told each other that they were stupid, that they were wrong, that in any case they were no more in the right than others who plugged along, who climbed up the ladder—but they loved their long days doing nothing, their lazy wakings, their mornings in bed with a pile of novels and science-fiction tales beside them, their walks at night along the quais, and the exciting feeling of freedom they felt on certain days, the vacation feeling that came over them every time they came back from interviewing in the provinces.

They knew, of course, that all this was false, that their freedom was only a snare. Their life was marked more deeply by their almost frantic searches for work when one of the agencies that employed them went bankrupt or was absorbed by a larger one (which happened frequently), by weekends when they had to count their cigarettes, by the time they wasted, on certain days, getting themselves invited to dinner.

They were in the middle of the most banal, the stupidest situation in the world. But it did no good to know that it was banal and stupid; they were in it nonetheless. The conflict between work and freedom had not been a rigorous one for a long time now, they admitted to each other; but it was nevertheless the thing that primarily made them what they were.

People who choose first of all to earn money, those who put their real plans off until later, until they are rich, are not necessarily wrong. Those who want only to live, for whom living means the greatest possible freedom, the pursuit of happiness alone, the exclusive satisfying of their desires or their instincts (Jérôme and Sylvie had adopted this vast program)—such people will always be unhappy. It is true, they recognized, that there are individuals to whom this sort of dilemma never presents itself, or hardly ever presents itself, either because they are too poor and do not have needs other than to eat a little bit better, have a little bit better living accommodations, work a little less, or because they are too well off from the very outset to understand the importance, or even the meaning, of such a distinction. But in our day and in our part of the world, more and more people are neither rich nor poor. They dream of wealth and might get rich: it is here that their troubles begin.

A hypothetical young man who studies for a while, then honorably fulfills his military obligations, finds himself at about the age of twenty-five as naked as the day he was born, though he is already virtually the possessor, by his very knowledge, of more money than he has ever dreamed of having. That is to say, he knows with certainty that a day will come when he will have his own apartment, his own country house, his own car, his own hi-fi system. It so happens, however, that these exciting promises unfortunately take time to be fulfilled. They belong, by their very nature, to a process that is also responsible, if one really thinks about it, for marriage, childbirth, the evolution of moral values, social attitudes, and human behavior patterns. In a word, the young man must settle down, and that will take him a good fifteen years.

Such a prospect is not comforting. Nobody commits himself to it without railing against it. "Well," the sharp young man says to himself, "am I going to have to spend my days behind glassed-in offices, instead of strolling through meadows in flower, am I going to catch myself hoping when the time comes for promotions, am I going to calculate my chances, plot, champ at the bit—I who dreamed of poetry, of night trains, of warm sands?" And in the belief that he is consoling himself, he falls into the snare of installment buying. He then is trapped, really trapped; the only thing left for him to do is to be patient. Alas, when he is at the end of his troubles the young man is no longer as young as he was, and to cap his troubles it may even seem to him that his life is behind him, that it was only hard work on his part, not an end in itself. And even if he is too wise, too prudent to dare tell himself such things (for his slow rise through the ranks will have given him a healthy dose of experience), it will nonetheless remain true that he will be around forty-five, and that establishing his primary and secondary residences and educating his children will have sufficed to fill the few hours that he has not devoted to his work.

Impatience, Jérôme and Sylvie told themselves, is a twentieth-century virtue. At twenty, when they had seen, or thought they had seen, what life could be, the sum of happiness that it held, the infinite conquests that it afforded, etc., they suddenly found that they would not have the strength to wait. Like others, they could get to where they were going, but all they wanted was to have gotten there. In this respect they were doubtless what people usually call intellectuals.

For everything made them seem in the wrong—life itself, first of all. They wanted to enjoy life, but everywhere around them joy was confused with possessing. They wanted to stay free—innocent almost—but years went by even so, and brought them nothing. Other people got

ahead, burdened with chains perhaps, but they got nowhere at all. Others came around to seeing wealth only as
an end, but they had no money at all.

They kept telling themselves that they were not the
worst off. They were perhaps right. But modern life ex-
acerbated their unhappiness, while it erased the unhappiness of others: other people were on the right track. The
two of them didn't amount to much: cheap-Jacks, free-
lancers, lunatics. It is true, on the other hand, that in a
certain sense time was working for them, that they had
images of a possible world that might appear to be exciting. This was, they both agreed, scant comfort.

THEY HAD SETTLED DOWN IN THE PROVISORY. They worked the way other people study; they chose what hours they would work. They loitered about as only students know how to loiter.

But dangers lay in wait for them on every hand. They would have liked their story to be a happy one; too often it was only the story of a threatened happiness. They were still young, but time was hurrying by. An overaged student has something ominous about him; a failure, a mediocre person, something more ominous still. They were afraid.

They had free time, but time also worked against them. Bills for gas, electricity, the telephone had to be paid. They had to eat every day. They had to have clothes, repaint the walls, change the sheets, send out the laundry, have shirts ironed, buy shoes, take the train, buy furniture.

At times the question of money swallowed them whole. They never stopped thinking about it. In a large measure even their emotional life was rigorously determined by it. When they had a bit of money, when they were a few francs ahead, their happiness together was indestructible; their love seemed to know no bounds. Their tastes, their imagination, their fantasy, their appetites merged into a freedom shared by both of them alike. But these moments were privileged. More often they had to fight with each other. At the first signs of a deficit, it was not rare for them to have it out with each other. They took up the cudgels for any trifle: for a hundred francs wasted, for a pair of stockings, for the dishes not done. They wouldn't speak to each other then for hours, for whole days. They would sit down opposite each other and eat quickly, keeping to themselves, avoiding the other's eye. They would each sit in one corner of the divan, backs half turned to each other. One of them would score innumerable points against the other.

Money came between them. It was a wall, a sort of obstacle they came up against at every turn. It was something worse than being poor: it was being uncomfortable, being restricted, having slender means. They lived in the closed world of their closed life, without a future, with no other opening outward but impossible miracles, crazy dreams that didn't hold together. They were suffocating. They felt themselves going under.

They could, of course, talk about something else: a book that had recently come out, a movie director, the war, other people. But it sometimes seemed to them that their only *real* conversations were about money, comfort, happiness. Their tone of voice rose then; the tension became greater. They talked, and as they talked, they were conscious of everything about themselves that was impossible, inaccessible, miserable. They got upset; they got too involved; they each felt they were being implicitly accused by the other. They drew up plans for vacations, for trips, for an apartment, and then destroyed them in a rage. It seemed to them that their realest life, seen in its true light, was something inconsistent, something that didn't exist. Then they would fall silent, and their silence would be full of bitterness. They had a grudge against life, and sometimes they were weak enough to nurse grudges against each other; they thought about their interrupted studies, their unappealing vacations, their mediocre life, their crowded apartment, their impossible dreams. They looked at each other, found each other ugly, badly dressed, lacking assurance, sullen. Automobiles slowly glided past them in the streets. Neon lights went on one by one in the public squares. People on the terraces of cafés looked like complacent fish. They hated everybody. They would walk home exhausted. They would go to bed without saying a word to each other.

All it would take for everything to tumble to ruins was a sudden change someday—an agency closing its doors, or their being found too old or too irregular in their work, or one of them getting sick. They had nothing before them, nothing behind them. They often thought of this anxiety-ridden subject. They came back to it endlessly, in spite of themselves. They envisioned themselves without work for months at a time, accepting ridiculous jobs in order to survive, borrowing, begging. They would then occasionally have moments of intense despair: they would dream of offices, fixed jobs, regular workdays, definite status. But these reversed images perhaps made them even more desperate. They could not recognize themselves in the guise of a sedentary office worker, however splendid that might be. They would decide that they hated hierarchies, and that solutions, miraculous or not, would come from somewhere else, from the world, from History.

They went on with their life full of ups and downs; it matched their natural inclinations. In a world full of imperfections it was not, they easily assured themselves, the most imperfect sort of life. They lived from day to day; they spent in six hours what had taken them three days to earn; they often borrowed money; they ate horrible fried foods, smoked their last cigarette together, searched for a metro ticket for two hours sometimes, wore made-over shirts, listened to second-hand phonograph records, hitch-hiked, and quite frequently went five or six weeks without changing the sheets. They were not far from thinking that, all in all, this life had its charms.

WHEN THE TWO OF THEM ENVISIONED their life, their way of doing things, their future, when with a sort of frenzy they gave themselves up to riotous visions of a better world, they sometimes told each other, with a sort of dull feeling of sadness, that they did not have clear ideas. Their view of the world was fuzzy, and the lucidity they claimed they had was often accompanied by vague fluctuations, ambiguous compromises, and varying considerations which tempered, minimized, or decreased the value of a spirit of good will that still was quite evident.

It seemed to them that this was a path, or an absence of a path, that defined them perfectly—and not only themselves, but everyone their age. The generations before them, they sometimes said to themselves, had no doubt been able to arrive at a more precise knowledge both of themselves and of the world they lived in. They would perhaps have liked to have been twenty years old during the Spanish Civil War or during the Resistance. They had, to tell the truth, long, leisurely talks about them. It seemed to them that the problems that presented themselves then, the problems they imagined must have been presented, were clearer, even though the necessity of finding an answer for them had been more pressing. All the questions they faced were traps.

It was a somewhat hypocritical nostalgia: the Algerian war had begun in their time; it was going on beneath their very eyes. It had almost no effect on them; they sometimes acted, but they rarely felt obliged to act. For a long time it did not occur to them that their life, their future, their conceptions might one day be turned topsy-turvy by it. This had once been partially true: their years as students had seen them participate, in a more spontaneous way, and almost enthusiastically, in the meetings and street demonstrations that had marked the beginnings of the war, the calling up of reserves, and above all, the advent of *gaullisme*. An almost immediate relationship was established between these actions, however limited they might be, and the object to which they were applied. Given the circumstances, one could not seriously have taken them to task for being wrong. The war went on; *gaullisme* set in; Jérôme and Sylvie gave up their studies.

Publicity circles generally leaned, almost mythologically, to the left, but were more easily definable by their technocracy, their cult of efficiency, modernity, complexity, the taste for future-oriented speculation, their rather demagogic orientation toward sociology, and the quite widespread opinion that nine people out of ten were idiots just barely capable of chanting the praises of anything and anybody in chorus. In these circles the right thing to do was to scorn every day-to-day policy, and to embrace history only by the century. It also turned out that *gaullisme* was really an adequate solution, infinitely more dynamic than people everywhere had predicted it would be, a solution whose danger was always somewhere else than where it was thought to be.

The war went on, however, even though it seemed to them to be only an episode, an almost secondary fact. They had an uneasy conscience about it, of course. But in the last analysis, if they felt responsible at all, it was only insofar as they remembered having once felt concerned, or be-

cause they adhered almost out of habit to moral impera-
tives of a very general scope. This indifference could have
been a measure of how vain, or perhaps how cowardly, a
fair number of their ardors were. But that was not the
question: they had seen, almost with surprise, some of
their former friends launch themselves, timidly or whole-
heartedly, into aid for the Algerian National Liberation
Front. They had misunderstood their reasons, not being
able to take seriously either a romantic explanation, which
rather amused them, or a political explanation, which
almost completely escaped them. As for themselves, they
had resolved the problem in a much simpler way: Jérôme
and three of his friends, with the help of precious testi-
mony in their favor and supporting documents, managed
to get out of military service just in time.

It was the Algerian war, however, and it alone, that protected them from themselves for two years. They might
well have aged more, or more rapidly. But it was neither
to their decisiveness, nor to their will, nor even—whatever
they might have said—to their sense of humor that they
owed the fact that for some time to come they could escape
a future which they willingly painted in the darkest of
colors. The events in 1961 and 1962, from the Algerian
putsch to the dead of Charonne, which marked the end of
the war, made them forget their usual preoccupations, or
rather, put them between parentheses; this was temporary,
but singularly effective. The most pessimistic predictions,
the fear of never getting out of their situation, of ending
up with something seedy and skimpy, on certain days appeared much less frightening than what was happening
right under their noses, what threatened them every day.

It was a sad and violent time. Housewives hoarded kilos

of sugar, bottles of oil, cans of tuna, coffee, condensed milk. Squads of *gardes mobiles,* helmeted, dressed in black oilskins and boots, with rifles in their hands, strolled slowly along the boulevard Sébastopol.

Because they often had in the back seat of their car back numbers of newspapers that there was every reason to believe certain touchy minds would find demoralizing, subversive, or simply liberal—*Le Monde, Libération, France-Observateur*—even Jérôme or Sylvie or their friends came to have furtive fears and disturbing fantasies. They were being followed, the license number of their car was being taken down, they were being spied on, a trap was being set for them: five drunk legionnaires would be out for their hides and leave them for dead on the wet pavement at the corner of a dark street in a tough neighborhood. . . .

This sudden entry of martyrdom into their daily lives (which sometimes turned into an obsession and was characteristic, it seemed to them, of a certain commonly held attitude) gave days, events, thoughts a particular coloration. Images of blood, explosions, violence, terror were always in their minds. It might seem, on certain days, that they were ready for anything; but the next day life was fragile, the future somber. They dreamed of exile, peaceful countrysides, leisurely cruises. They would have liked to live in England, where the police have the reputation of being respectful of the human person. And all through the winter, as the cease-fire drew closer, they dreamed of the coming spring, their coming vacations, the next year when fratricidal passions would die, as the newspapers put it, when it would again be possible to stroll about, to walk at night with a tranquil heart and one's person safe and sound.

The pressure of events led them to take a stand. Their

commitment was only skin-deep, of course; at no time did they feel deeply concerned. Their political conscience (what there was of it as an organized, reflective entity and not a magma of more or less set opinions) was situated, they thought, short of the Algerian problem, or beyond it, on the level of choices more utopian than real, on the level of general debates which had few chances of leading to concerted actions—they recognized this and regretted it. They nonetheless joined the Anti-Fascist Committee that had just been set up in their neighborhood. They sometimes got up at five in the morning to go along with three or four others to put up posters calling on people to be vigilant, denouncing guilty parties and their accomplices, stigmatizing the cowardly assaults, honoring the innocent victims. They passed out petitions to every house on their street; they went three or four times to guard threatened buildings.

They took part in a few demonstrations. On those days buses rolled by without placards, cafés closed early, people hurried home. They were frightened all day. They went out feeling ill at ease. It was five o'clock; it was drizzling. They looked at the other demonstrators with tense little smiles, looked for their friends, tried to talk about something else. Then ranks formed, began to move, stopped. From the middle of the crowd around them they saw in front of them a great expanse of wet and dismal-looking asphalt, then the thick black line of special riot squads all along the boulevard. Rows of midnight-blue trucks with barred windows passed by in the distance. They marked time, holding each other by the hand, damp with sweat, hardly daring to shout, dispersing at a run on the first signal.

It didn't amount to much. They were the first to realize

this, and often wondered what they were doing in the middle of the crowd, in the cold, in the rain, in these sinister neighborhoods: Bastille, Nation, Hôtel de Ville. They would have liked something to prove to them that what they were doing was important, necessary, irreplaceable, that their fearful efforts had a meaning for them, were something they needed, something that could help them to know themselves, transform themselves, live. But there was nothing. Their real life was elsewhere, in the near or distant future, also full of threats, but more subtle, more cunning threats: impalpable traps, magic snares.

The murders at Issy-les-Moulineux and the brief demonstration that followed marked the end of their activities as militants. The Anti-Fascist Committee in their neighborhood met once more and vowed to be even more active. But on the eve of vacation time, even simple vigilance seemed to have no further reason for being.

THEY COULD NOT HAVE SAID EXACTLY what had changed with the end of the war. For a long time it seemed to them that the only impression that they got was of something ended, concluded, over and done with. Not a happy ending, not a melodramatic turn of events, but on the contrary a sad, long-drawn-out ending leaving behind it a feeling of emptiness, of bitterness, drowning memories in shadow. Time had dragged by, had fled; an age was over; it was peacetime again, a peace that they had never known; the war was drawing to a close. In one stroke seven years were suddenly a thing of the past: their years as students, the years that they had met other people, the best years of their lives.

Perhaps nothing had changed. On occasion they still sat at their windows, looked out at the courtyard, the little gardens, the chestnut tree; they still listened to the birds sing. Other books, other records had piled up on the shaky shelves. The diamond needle on the phonograph was beginning to wear out.

Their work was still the same; they conducted the same interviews as they had three years before. How do you shave? Do you shine your shoes? They had seen movies and seen them over again, taken a few trips, discovered other restaurants. They had bought shirts and shoes, sweaters and skirts, dishes, sheets, knickknacks.

What was new was so insidious, so nebulous, so closely linked to their own particular history, to their dreams.

They were tired. They had gotten older, no doubt about it. On certain days they had the impression that they had not yet begun to live. But more and more the life that they were leading seemed fragile, ephemeral to them, and they felt they had no strength left, as if waiting, being uncomfortable, having limited means had worn them out, as if everything—the unfulfilled desires, the imperfect joys, the wasted time—had been natural.

At times they would have liked everything to last, nothing to budge. They had only to let themselves go. Their life would lull them. It would go on through the months, through all the years almost without changing, without ever imposing a strain on them. It would be only the harmonious succession of days and nights, an almost imperceptible modulation, the endless reprise of the same themes, a continuous happiness, a constant savor that no upheaval, no tragic event, no sudden change of fortune would ever put into question.

At other times they were at the end of their rope. They wanted to fight and win. They wanted to battle, to conquer their happiness. But how were they to fight? Against whom? Against what? They lived in a strange, iridescent world, the shimmering universe of a mercantile civilization, the prisons of abundance, the fascinating snares of happiness.

Where were the dangers? Where were the threats? Millions of men once fought—and still fight—for bread. Jérôme and Sylvie hardly thought that one could fight for a Chesterfield divan. But that would have been the slogan most likely to have mobilized them. Programs, plans, seemed to have nothing to do with them: they didn't care at all about early retirement, longer vacations, free lunches, thirty-hour weeks. They wanted superabundance:

they dreamed of Clément turntables, of deserted beaches all for themselves, of trips around the world, of palaces.

The enemy was invisible. Or rather, it was within them. It had rotted them, made them gangrenous, ravaged them. They were dupes, docile little creatures, faithful reflections of a world that sneered at them. They were buried to the neck in a cake they would never have more than the crumbs of.

For a long time the crises they had gone through had little effect on their good humor. They did not seem fatal; they put nothing in question. They often told each other that friendship protected them. The way the group stuck together was a sure guarantee, a stable reference point, a force they could count on. They felt they were right because they knew they were good friends, and they loved nothing so much as to be together at one or another of each other's houses on certain particularly difficult days at the end of the month, sitting down to a potful of potatoes and bacon and sharing their last cigarettes in the most fraternal spirit possible.

But their friendships too were coming apart. On certain evenings in the closed space of their tiny rooms, the couples gathered together would exchange hostile looks and remarks. On certain evenings they would finally realize that their beautiful friendships, their vocabulary that was almost a secret language, their intimate gags, this common world, this common language, these common gestures that they had created had nothing to do with anything else: it was a shriveled-up universe, a panting world that led nowhere. Their life was not a conquest; it was falling into dust, blowing away. They then realized how much they were condemned to habit, to inertia. They bored each

other, as if there had never been anything except a void between them. For a long time, puns, getting drunk together,
walks in the forest, huge meals, long discussions about a
film, plans, gossip had substituted for adventure, history,
truth. But they were only hollow words, empty gestures,
with no density, no opening outward, no future, words repeated a thousand times, hands shaken a thousand times, a
ritual that no longer protected them.

They would then try for an hour to agree on what film
they would go see. They would chatter aimlessly, guess at
riddles, or play twenty questions. Once by themselves, each
couple would speak bitterly about the others, and at times
about themselves. They would talk nostalgically about
their bygone youth; they would remember having been
enthusiastic, spontaneous, with a wealth of real plans,
sumptuous images, desires. They dreamed of making new
friends, but they could hardly imagine what they would
be like.

Slowly but inexorably the group broke up. With a
suddenness that sometimes was cruel, in hardly more than
a few weeks, it became evident to some of them that the
good old days would never again be possible. They were
too weary, the world around them too exacting. Those
who had lived in rooms without running water, who had
lunched on a quarter of a loaf of bread, who had thought
they were living just as they pleased, who had tugged at
the rope without its ever breaking, one fine day put down
roots: almost naturally, almost objectively they could no
longer resist the temptation of steady work, a good job,
bonuses, months with double pay.

Almost all their friends succumbed, one after the other.

Times of security succeeded times without attachments. "We can't go on like this," they would say, and this "like this" was a vague gesture, everything at once: leading a wild life, nights that were too short, potatoes, threadbare jackets, thankless tasks, subways.

Little by little, without really noticing, Jérôme and Sylvie found that they were almost without friends. Friendship, it seemed to them, was possible only when they stuck together, when they lived the same life. But let one couple suddenly acquire what for the other was almost a fortune or the promise of a fortune to come, and let the other couple prize the freedom they still had, and two worlds seemed to clash. These were not temporary disagreements, but serious breaks, deep splits, wounds that did not heal by themselves. When they met there was now a basic mistrust which would have been impossible a few months before. Their talk was forced; they seemed constantly to be flinging down the gauntlet.

Jérôme and Sylvie were stern, unjust. They talked of treason, of surrender. They were pleased to witness the terrifying ravages money could cause, they said, in people who had given up everything for it, ravages they had thus far escaped, they thought. They saw their former friends settle down with almost no difficulty, almost too comfortably, in a rigid hierarchy, and cling to the world they were entering without a single step backward. They saw them humiliate themselves, ingratiate themselves, fool themselves about their power, their influence, their responsibility. They thought they had discovered through these friends the exact opposite of their own world: the world that justified, all in a lump, money, work, advertising, talent, a world that valued experience, a world that scorned them, the serious world of executives, the world of power. They came close to thinking that their former friends were letting themselves be had.

They did not scorn money. Perhaps, on the contrary, they liked it too much. They would have liked security, certainly, a clear path into the future. They paid close attention to all the signs of permanence; they wanted to be rich. And if they still resisted getting rich, it was because they didn't need a salary; their imagination, their cultural background allowed them to think only in millions.

They often took walks in the evening, sniffing the wind, window-shopping. They left behind them the nearby thirteenth arrondissement, which they hardly knew except for the avenue des Gobelins (because it had four movie theaters), avoided the sinister rue Cuvier, which would have led them only to the even more sinister environs of the gare d'Austerlitz, and almost invariably took the rue Monge, then the rue des Écoles, reached Saint-Michel, Saint-Germain, and from there, depending on the day or the season, went on to the Palais Royal, the Opéra, or the gare Montparnasse, Vavin, rue d'Assas, Saint-Sulpice, the Luxembourg. They walked along slowly. They stopped in front of each antique shop, glued their eyes to the dim shop windows, made out through the grills the reddish reflections of a leather couch, the leaf decorations of a porcelain plate or platter, the gleam of a cut-crystal tumbler or a copper candlestick, the delicate curves of a caned chair.

From one stopping point to another—antique dealers, bookstores, record shops, restaurant menus, travel agencies, haberdasheries, tailors' shops, cheese merchants, shoe stores, confectioners, de luxe pork stores, stationers—their itineraries made up their real universe: it was there that their ambitions, their hopes lay. Their real life was there, the life they wanted to know, the life they wanted to live: it was for these salmon, these rugs, these crystal pieces that a shopgirl and a hairdresser had brought them into the world twenty-five years earlier.

When, next day, life again crushed them, when the great advertising machine of which they were the tiny pawns started up once again, it seemed to them that they had not completely forgotten the shadowy marvels, the unveiled secrets of their fervent nocturnal quest. They sat across from people who believe in the brand names, the slogans, the images offered them, who eat the fat of quartered beef and find its vegetable aroma and hazelnut smell delicious. (But did they themselves not find certain posters beautiful, certain slogans wonderful, certain ads for films the product of genius—without really knowing why, and with the curious, almost worrisome feeling that something was escaping them?) They sat down and started their tape-recorders, they said "hmm, hmm" in the right tone of voice, they faked their interviews, they threw analyses together, they dreamed, vaguely, of something else.

How to make a fortune? It was an insoluble problem. And yet it seemed to them that every day isolated individuals managed, all on their own, to solve it perfectly. And these examples to follow (eternal guarantees of the intellectual and moral vigor of France), with their smiling, cautious, sly, determined faces, healthy, decisive, and modest, were so many pious images for the patience and guidance of others, those who are stagnating, marking time, champing at the bit, biting the dust.

They knew all about the rise of these darlings of Fortune to the top: knights of industry, incorruptible graduates of the École Polytechnique, financial sharks, literary figures who never scratched a word out, globe-trotters, pioneers, packaged-soup-powder merchants, suburban prospectors, crooners, playboys, gold-hunters, businessmen who handle millions. Their story was simple. They were still young and had kept their good looks, with the little light of experience in the depths of their eyes, the gray temples from the dark years, the frank, warm smile that hid sharp teeth, the opposable thumbs, the charming voice.

They could easily see themselves in these roles. They would have three acts of a play in the bottom of a drawer. Their garden would contain oil, uranium. They would live for a long time in misery, uncomfortable circumstances, uncertainty. They would dream of taking, just once, a first-class car on the subway. Then suddenly—fierce, disheveled, unexpected, bursting like a clap of thunder—a Fortune! Their play would be accepted, their subterranean deposit discovered, their genius confirmed. Contracts would rain down on them and they would light their Havana cigars with thousand-franc bills.

It would happen on a morning just like any other. Three long narrow envelopes with imposing return addresses engraved in relief, with a neat, precise address typed on an IBM Executive, would have been slipped under the front door. Their hands would tremble a little as they opened them. It would be three checks with long strings of figures. Or else a letter:

DEAR SIR,
Mr. Podevin, your uncle, having died intestate . . .

and they would pass their hands over their faces, not believing their eyes, thinking they were still dreaming; they would throw the window wide open. . . .

So they dreamed, the happy imbeciles: of inheritances, of having the winning number in a lottery, of winning bets at the races. The bank at Monte Carlo would blow up. There would be a sack left in a baggage rack in a deserted railway car—bundles of big bills. They would find a pearl necklace in a dozen oysters, or else a pair of priceless Boulle armchairs in the home of an illiterate Poitou peasant.

They would get carried away. For whole hours, sometimes for days, a frenetic desire to be rich, immediately, enormously rich, forever, would come over them and not let go. It was a mad, unhealthy, oppressive desire, which seemed to govern their slightest gesture. Possessing a fortune became their opium. They were intoxicated by it.

They gave themselves up unreservedly to deliriums of the imagination. Wherever they went they noticed only money. They had nightmares about millions, about jewels.

They often went to big sales at auction houses: Drouot, Galliéra. They mingled with gentlemen who were examining the paintings, catalogue in hand. They saw pastels by Degas, rare stamps, stupid pieces of goldwork, fragile editions of La Fontaine or Crébillon sumptuously bound by Lederer, admirable authentic furniture by Claude Séné or d'Œhlenberg, gold and silver snuffboxes go on the auction block. The auctioneer would offer them for inspection; a few serious-looking people would come up to sniff at them; a murmur would pass through the hall. The bidding would begin. Prices would climb. Then the gavel would fall, it would all be over, the object would disappear; five or ten million francs would have passed by within reach of their hands.

They sometimes followed the buyers; usually these happy mortals were only underlings, employees of antique dealers, private secretaries, straw men. They led them to the thresholds of austere houses, voie Oswaldo-Cruz, boulevard Beauséjour, rue Maspéro, rue Spontini, Villa Saïd, avenue du Roule. Beyond the grills, beyond the boxwood hedges, the gravel paths, curtains that were sometimes not quite closed afforded them a glimpse of huge rooms, dimly lit; they could make out the vague contours of the couches and armchairs, the imprecise touches of paint of an impressionist canvas. And they would go back the way they had come, wistful, irritated.

One day they even dreamed of stealing. They spent a long time imagining themselves dressed in black with a tiny flashlight in their hand, a jimmy, a glass-cutter in their pocket, creeping into a building at nightfall, making their way to the cellar, forcing the simple lock of a dumb-waiter, reaching the kitchen. It would be the apartment of a diplomat on a mission, of a shady financier whose tastes were nonetheless perfect, of a great dilettante, of a knowledgeable lover of the arts. They would know every corner of the place. They would know where to find the little twelfth-century virgin, the oval panel by Sebastiano del Piombo, the Fragonard wash drawing, the two little Renoirs, the little Boudin, the Atlan, the Max Ernst, the de Staël, the coins, the music boxes, the candy boxes, the silverware, the Delft porcelains. Their movements would be precise and deliberate, as if they had practiced them over and over. They would move about without hurrying, sure of themselves, efficient, imperturbable, unruffled, Arsène Lupins of the modern era. Not a muscle of their face would twitch. The windows would be broken one by one; one by one the canvases would be detached from the wall, taken out of their frames.

Their car would be waiting downstairs. They would have filled it with gas the night before. Their passports would be in order. They would long have been ready to leave. Their trunks would await them in Brussels. They would set out for Belgium; go across the border with no difficulty. Then little by little, without undue haste, they would resell their booty in Luxemburg, Antwerp, Amsterdam, London, the United States, South America. They would go around the world. They would wander for a long time, wherever fancy led them. They would finally settle down in a country with an agreeable climate. Somewhere, on the shores of the Italian lakes, at Dubrovnik, in the Balearic Islands, at Cefalù, they would buy a large house in white stone, hidden in the middle of a park.

They did none of this, of course. They didn't even buy a ticket for the national lottery. The furthest they went was to show a relentlessness at poker games (which they had just discovered, and which were about to become the last refuge of their worn-out friendships) which at times might have appeared suspect. On certain weeks they played up to three or four games, each of which kept them up till dawn. They played for small stakes, such small stakes that they had only the foretaste of risk, the illusion of winning. And yet when with two meager pairs, or better yet a four-card flush, they threw on the table, all at once, a huge pile of chips worth three hundred old francs at the most and raked in the pot, when they were in the game for six hundred paper francs, lost them in three hands, then won them back, and more besides, in the next six hands, a triumphant little smile would cross their faces: they had forced their luck; their little show of courage had borne fruit. They were not far from feeling heroic.

An INTERVIEW ON AGRICULTURE took them all over France. They went to Lorraine, Saintonge, Picardy, Beauce, Limagne. They saw notaries from old families, wholesaler dealers whose trucks covered half of France, prosperous manufacturers, gentlemen farmers escorted at all times by a pack of large reddish dogs and watchful handymen.

The granaries were full to the brim with wheat; in the large paved yards shiny tractors stood nose to nose with the black cars of the owners. They went across the workers' dining room, the giant kitchen with women bustling about, the common room with a yellowed floor, where nobody moved about except on felt soles, with its imposing fireplace, a television set, winged armchairs, light-oak hutches, copper, pewter, porcelain. At the end of a narrow corridor, full of all sorts of smells, a door opened onto the office. It was a room that seemed quite small because it was so full of things. A master plan tacked to the wall next to an old crank telephone summed up the land being worked, the corn that had been sowed, the plans, the cash on hand, the due date of loans; an eloquent line gave witness to record production. On a table loaded with paid receipts, payslips, memoranda, and paper work, a register bound in black canvas, opened to the current date, allowed one to see the long columns of figures of a flourishing set of accounts. Framed certificates—bulls, milk cows, prize sows

—hung next to sections of cadastral maps, military maps, photos of herds and poultry yards, four-color advertising brochures for tractors, threshers, plows, seeders.

This was where they plugged in their tape-recorders. They gravely asked questions about the place of agriculture in modern life, the contradictions of rural French development plans, the farmer of tomorrow, the Common Market, the decisions of the government concerning wheat and sugar beets, free stabilization and parity of prices. But their minds were elsewhere. They watched themselves going and coming in the deserted house. They went up waxed stairways, went into rooms with closed shutters that smelled musty. Venerable pieces of furniture lay beneath gray canvas covers. They opened cupboards nine feet high, full of sheets perfumed with lavender, glass jars, silverware.

In the half-light of attics, they discovered unsuspected treasures. In endless cellars, tuns and barrels, jars full of oil and honey, casks of salt pork, hams cured with juniper berries, kegs of fruit brandy awaited them.

They wandered through resounding laundry rooms, storerooms for wood, storerooms for coal, fruit storerooms with row upon row of apples and pears on screens one atop the other, dairy rooms with their pronounced smell where balls of fresh butter gloriously marked with a damp print, cans of milk, bowls of fresh cream, of cream cheese, of *cancoillote* cheese lay heaped together.

They went through cattle barns, stables, workrooms, forges, sheds, bakeries where enormous round loaves of bread were baking, silos full to bursting with sacks, garages.

From the top of the water tower they could see the whole farm, enclosing on all four sides a large paved court with ogived doors, the poultry yard, the pigsty, the vegetable garden, the orchard, the road bordered with plane trees that led to the national highway, and all around, as far as the eye could see, the great yellow stripes of fields of wheat, forests, coppices, pastures, the straight black traces of the roads, on which the gleam of a car sped by from time to time, and the sinuous line of poplars along an almost invisible embanked river disappearing on the horizon as it flowed toward hazy hills.

Then other mirages popped into their minds like puffs of smoke. There were immense markets, endless shopping arcades, unheard-of restaurants. Everything imaginable to eat and drink was offered them. There were cases, wicker baskets, hampers, market baskets overflowing with big red or yellow apples, oblong pears, purple grapes. There were displays of mangoes and figs, of cantaloupes and watermelons, of lemons, of pomegranates, of sacks of almonds, of walnuts, of pistachio nuts, of boxes of Smyrna or Corinth raisins, of dried bananas, of candied fruit, of transparent yellow dried dates.

There were delicatessens, temples with a thousand columns, with ceilings loaded with hams and sausages, dark caves heaped with mountains of potted pork, of pork sausages coiled up like rope, barrels of sauerkraut, of purplish-blue olives, of salted anchovies, of cucumbers.

Or else, on each side of a street, a double hedge of milk-fed chickens, of wild boars hanging by the feet, of quarters of beef, of hares, of fat geese, of roe deer with glassy eyes.

They would go through grocery stores full of delicious

smells, through marvelous pastry shops with hundreds of tarts set out in rows, through splendid kitchens with a thousand copper cauldrons.

They would founder in abundance. They would let colossal markets go up. Paradises of hams, cheese, alcohol would spring up before their eyes. Tables all ready to sit down to would be offered them, laid with dazzling white napkins, flowers sown in profusion, crystal services and precious dishes. There would be dozens of pâtés baked in a crust, terrines, salmon, pike, trout, lobster, beribboned legs of lamb with horn and silver handles, hares and quails, smoking wild boars, cheeses as big as millstones, armies of bottles.

Locomotives would appear, pulling cars full of fat cattle; trucks of bleating lambs would come into town; boxes of lobsters would be piled in pyramids. Millions of loaves of bread would come out of thousands of ovens. Tons of coffee would be unloaded off ships.

Then, still farther away—and they half closed their eyes —they would see cities a hundred stories high going up, in the middle of forests and lawns, along rivers, at the gates of deserts, or overlooking the sea on vast plazas paved in marble.

They would walk along façades of steel, rare woods, glass, marble. In the main foyer, along a cut-glass wall that reflected millions of rainbows out into the whole city, a waterfall would come down from the fiftieth floor, surrounded by the dizzying spirals of two aluminum staircases.

Elevators would whisk them away. They would follow meandering corridors, climb crystal steps, stride along galleries bathed with light, with row upon row of statues and flowers as far as the eye could see, where limpid streams would flow on beds of colored pebbles.

Doors would open before them. They would discover outdoor swimming pools, patios, reading rooms, sound-proof rooms, theaters, aviaries, gardens, aquariums, tiny museums planned for themselves alone, with four Flemish portraits at the four canted corners of a little room. Some rooms would be only rocks, others only jungles; in others the sea would dash in; in still others peacocks would promenade. Thousands of oriflammes would hang from the ceiling of a circular room. Endless labyrinths would resound with soft music; a room with extravagant forms would have no other apparent function than to set off interminable echoes; the ground in another would repro-duce, according to the hour of the day, the variable scheme of a very complicated game.

In immense basements, docile machines would be at work, as far as the eye could see.

They would let themselves go on from one marvel to another, from one surprise to another. It was enough for them to be alive, to be there, for the whole world to offer itself. Their ships, their trains, their rockets furrowed the whole planet. The world belonged to them with its prov-inces covered with wheat, its seas teeming with fish, its summits, its deserts, its flowering countrysides, its beaches, its islands, its trees, its treasures, its huge factories, long abandoned, buried beneath the ground, where the finest wool, the brightest silks were woven for them.

They would come to know innumerable kinds of hap-piness. They would let themselves be carried off at a gallop by wild horses, across rolling plains of tall grasses. They would scale the highest summits. They would ski down steep slopes dotted with giant pines. They would swim in still lakes. They would walk in a driving rain, breathing in the smell of wet grass. They would stretch out in the sun. Looking down from a peak they would discover valleys covered with wild flowers. They would walk in boundless forests. They would make love in rooms full of shadows, thick rugs, deep divans.

Then they dreamed of precious porcelains, of décors with exotic birds, of leather-bound books printed in Elzévir type on Japanese paper with large uncut white margins where the eye could pause with delight, of mahogany tables, of silk or linen clothes, soft and comfortable and colorful, of bright spacious rooms, of flowers by the armful, of Bokhara rugs, of bounding Dobermans.

Their bodies, their gestures, were infinitely beautiful, their gaze serene, their hearts transparent, their smiles bright.

And in a brief apotheosis they would see giant palaces being constructed. On leveled plains thousands of bonfires would be lit; millions of men would come to sing *The Messiah*. On colossal terraces ten thousand brasses would play Verdi's *Requiem*. Poems would be engraved in the sides of mountains. Gardens would spring up in the deserts. Entire cities would be merely frescoes.

But these sparkling images, all these images that crowded in on them, that rushed before them, that flowed by in a jerky, inexhaustible stream, these images of dizziness, speed, light, triumph seemed to them at first to follow one after the other with a surprising inevitability, as if there had suddenly appeared before their startled eyes a perfect landscape, a spectacular and triumphant whole, a complete image of the world, a coherent structure that they could at last understand, decipher. It seemed to them at first that their sensations were ten times as numerous, that their faculties for seeing and feeling were infinitely amplified, that a marvelous happiness accompanied their slightest gesture, set their steps in rhythm, permeated their life: the world was coming their way, they were going out to meet the world, they were endlessly discovering it. Their life was love and intoxication. Their passion knew no bounds; their freedom knew no constraint.

But they were suffocating beneath the accumulation of details. The images grew blurred, grew fuzzy. They could retain only a few tag-ends of them, vague and confused, fragile, obsessive and stupid, impoverished. No longer a movement of the whole, but only isolated pictures, no longer a serene unity, but only a tense fragmentation, as if these images had never been anything but very distant, overdarkened reflections, allusive, illusory twinklings that vanished almost the moment they appeared, dust: the ridiculous projection of their most awkward desires, an impalpable dust cloud of meager splendors, scraps of dreams they would never be able to take hold of.

They thought they could imagine happiness; they thought their fantasy was free, magnificent, permeated the universe in successive waves. They thought they need only walk for walking to become a joy. But they found themselves alone, motionless, a bit empty. An icy gray plain, an arid steppe: no palace towered at the gates of deserts, no esplanade served as a horizon for them.

And nothing was left of this desperate search for happiness, of the marvelous feeling of having almost been able for an instant to catch a glimpse of it, to guess what it was like, of this immense motionless conquest, of these horizons discovered, of these pleasures foreseen, of everything that was perhaps possible beneath this imperfect dream. Nothing was left of this eagerness, which was still gauche and embarrassed but perhaps full of new emotions nonetheless, new needs that bordered on the inexpressible. They opened their eyes, heard once again the sound of their voices, the confused muttering of the person they were talking to, the purring of the tape-recorder motor. They saw opposite them, next to a gunrack with five hunting rifles hung one above the other, with patinated stocks and barrels shining with grease, the multicolored puzzle of the official cadastral survey map, in the center of which they recognized, almost without surprise, the nearly perfect rectangle of the farm, the gray stripe of the little road, the little dots of plane trees in quincunxes, the heavier lines of the national highways.

And later still they themselves were on that little gray road lined with plane trees. They were that shining little dot on the long black road. They were a little island of poverty in the great sea of abundance. They saw around them the great yellow fields with little red dots of poppies. They felt crushed.

# Part Two

T<small>HEY TRIED TO ESCAPE.</small>

One cannot live very long amid frenzy. The tension was too great in this world that promised so much and gave nothing. They were at the end of their patience. They seemed suddenly to realize one day that they needed a refuge.

They were marking time in Paris. They were no longer getting ahead. And they sometimes imagined themselves (each trying to outdo the other with that superabundance of false details that marked each of their dreams) as petits bourgeois forty years old. Jérôme would be a director of a door-to-door selling network (Family Protection, Soap for the Blind, Needy Students); Sylvie would be a good housewife, with their tidy apartment, their little car, the little family *pension* where they would spend all their vacations, their television set. Or else they would see themselves as just the opposite, and this was still worse: overage bohemians, in turtlenecks and velvet pants, at the same sidewalk café in Saint-Germain or Montparnasse each night, eking out an existence through rare strokes of luck, shabby to the very ends of their black fingernails.

They would dream of living in the country, safe from all temptation. Their life would be frugal and clear as crystal. They would have a white stone house at the entrance of a village, warm corduroy pants, heavy shoes, a ski jacket, a steel-tipped cane, a hat, and they would take long walks in the forest every day. Then they would come back home; they would prepare tea and toast, as the English do; they would put huge logs in the fireplace; they would put a quartet they never tired of hearing on the phonograph; they would read the great novels they had never had time to read; they would receive their friends.

These imaginary flights to the country were frequent, but they rarely got to the stage of real planning. Two or three times, it is true, they idly wondered what sort of jobs they could get in the country. There weren't any. The thought of being schoolteachers came to them one day, but they immediately loathed the idea, thinking of the over-crowded classes, the hectic days. They talked vaguely of becoming traveling librarians, or of going to make pottery in an abandoned country house in Provence. Then they conceived the happy notion of living in Paris only three days a week, earning enough money there to live com-fortably in the Yonne or the Loiret the rest of the time. But these embryonic departures never developed into much of anything. They never envisaged the real pos-sibilities—or rather, real impossibilities—of them.

They dreamed of giving up their work, of letting every-thing go, of starting out with no set plans. They dreamed of starting over from scratch, of beginning all over on a differ-ent footing. They dreamed of sharp breaks and goodbyes.

The idea, however, made its inroads, and slowly came to stick in their minds. In mid-September of 1962, when they got back from a mediocre vacation spoiled by rain and their lack of money, they seemed to have made up their minds. An ad appeared in *Le Monde* during the first days of October, offering teaching jobs in Tunisia. They hesitated. It was not the ideal chance—they had dreamed of the Indies, the United States, Mexico. It was only a run-of-the-mill, ordinary offer, which promised neither lots of money nor adventure. They did not feel tempted. But they had friends in Tunis, former high school and university classmates, and then there was the warm climate, the blue Mediterranean, the promise of another life, a real departure, different work. They agreed they would apply. They were given the jobs.

Real departures are planned long in advance. This one was a fiasco. It resembled a hasty escape. For two weeks they ran from office to office, for medical examinations, for passports, for visas, for tickets, for baggage. Then four days before they were to leave they learned that Sylvie, who had two advanced teaching certificates, had been appointed to the Technical High School in Sfax, two hundred and seventy kilometers from Tunis, and Jérôme, who had had only one year of preparation for teaching, was appointed to teach grade school in Maharès, thirty-five kilometers farther away.

It was bad news. They wanted to give up the whole thing. They had wanted to go, they had thought they were going to Tunis, where friends were waiting for them, where a place to live had been rented for them. But it was too late. They had sublet their apartment, bought their tickets, given their good-bye party. They had been ready to leave for a long time. And then Sfax, a place they hardly recognized the name of, was the end of the world, the desert. Yet it did not even displease them, what with their strong liking for extreme situations, to think that they were going to be cut off from everything, far away from everything, isolated as they had never been before. They agreed, however, that a post as a grade school teacher was, if not too much of a comedown, at least too hard a job.

Jérôme managed to have his contract canceled: one salary would give them money to live on until he found some sort of work once he got there.

So they left. Friends went with them to the station, and on the morning of the twenty-third of October, with four trunks of books and a folding bed, they went aboard the "Commandant-Crubellier" at Marseille, bound for Tunis. The sea was rough and lunch was not good. They were ill, took tablets, slept soundly. The next day they sighted Tunis. The weather was fine. They smiled at each other. They saw an island that someone said was named L'Ile Plane, then stretches of long, narrow beach, and after la Goulette, flights of migratory birds on the lake.

They were happy they had left. It seemed to them that they were emerging from a hell of crowded subways, nights that were too short, toothaches, uncertainties. They couldn't see things clearly. Their life had been a sort of endless dance on a tightrope which led nowhere: empty hunger pangs, a naked desire, boundless and helpless. They felt exhausted. They were leaving to bury themselves, to forget, to find peace.

The sun was shining. The ship sailed slowly, silently, down the narrow channel. On the road right next to it people standing in open cars waved to them. There were motionless little white clouds in the sky. It was already hot. The plates of the topside were warm. On the deck below them, sailors were piling up the deck chairs, rolling up the long tarred canvases that protected the holds. Lines were forming at the gangplanks.

They arrived at Sfax two days later, about two o'clock in the afternoon after a seven-hour train trip. The heat was

overwhelming. Opposite the station, a tiny pink and white
building, was an endless avenue, gray with dust, planted
with ugly palm trees, lined with new buildings. A few
minutes after the train pulled in, after the few scattered
cars and motorbikes had left, the city fell once again into
total silence.

They left their valises at the baggage-checking desk.
They started down the avenue, which was called the
avenue Bourguiba, and came to a restaurant about three
hundred yards away. A huge adjustable ventilator on the
wall hummed irregularly. A few dozen flies had congre-
gated on the sticky tables covered with oilcloth, and a
poorly shaved waiter chased them away with a nonchalant
wave of a napkin. For two hundred francs they had a tuna
salad and a veal cutlet milanese.

Then they looked for a hotel, got a room, and had their
bags brought up. They washed their hands and faces, lay
down for a minute, changed clothes, came downstairs
again. Sylvie went to the Technical High School; Jérôme
waited for her outside on a bench. Around four o'clock,
Sfax slowly began to wake up again. Hundreds of children
appeared, then veiled women, policemen dressed in gray
poplin, beggars, carts, donkeys, immaculate bourgeois.

Sylvie came out with her teaching schedule in her hand.
They walked around again; they drank a stein of beer and
ate olives and salted almonds. Newspaper vendors were
selling the *Figaro* of two days before. They had arrived.

The next day Sylvie met some of her future colleagues.
They helped them find an apartment. There were, to
begin with, three enormous, completely empty rooms with
high ceilings. A long corridor led to a little square room
where five doors opened on the three bedrooms, a bath-

room, and an immense kitchen. Two balconies overlooked a little fishing port, Basin A of the south channel, which somewhat resembled Saint-Tropez, and a lagoon that stank. They took their first walk in the Arab quarter, bought box springs and a hair mattress, two rattan chairs, four rope stools, two tables, a thick esparto-grass mat decorated with unusual red motifs.

Then Sylvie began teaching. Day by day they settled down. Their trunks, which had come as hold baggage, arrived. They unpacked the books, the records, the phonograph, the knickknacks. They made lampshades out of large sheets of red, gray, green blotting paper. They bought long, rough-hewn pieces of lumber and perforated bricks and covered half of two walls with shelves. They pasted up dozens of reproductions on all the walls, and photographs of all their friends on one section in plain sight.

It was a cold and dreary place. What with the walls that were too high, covered in a sort of ocher-yellow limewash that was peeling off in great chunks, the floors uniformly tiled in large colorless squares, the useless space, everything was too large, too bare, for them to feel at home there. There should have been five or six of them, good friends, eating, drinking, talking. But they were alone, lost. The living room still gave off a certain warmth, what with its folding bed covered with a little mattress and a multi-colored bedspread, with the thick mat with a few cushions thrown on it, with, above all, their books—the row of Pléiade editions, the sets of magazines, the four Tisnés— and with the knickknacks, the records, the big nautical chart, the "Festival of the Carrousel," everything that not so long ago had been the décor of their other life, everything that in this universe of sand and stone took them

back toward the rue de Quartrefages, toward the tree that
stayed green so long, toward the little gardens. Lying on
their bellies on the mat, with a tiny cup of Turkish coffee
next to them, they would listen to the Kreutzer sonata,
the Archduke trio, *Death and the Maiden,* and it was as if
the music, which took on an astonishing resonance in this
huge, barely furnished room, almost a public hall, began
to live in it and suddenly transformed it. It was a guest, a
very dear friend, who had dropped out of sight and been
found again by chance, who shared their meals, who spoke
to them of Paris, who on this cool November evening in
this foreign town where nothing belonged to them, where
they did not feel comfortable, led them back, allowed them
to experience once again an almost forgotten feeling of
complicity, of life shared. It was as if in a narrow perimeter
—the surface of the mat, the two rows of shelves, the
record player, the circle of light shed by the cylindrical
lampshade—a protected zone, which neither time nor distance could penetrate, had managed to take root and survive. But all around them was exile, the unknown: the
long corridor where steps resounded too loudly; the immense, ice-cold, hostile bedroom with its one piece of
furniture, a wide bed that was too hard and smelled of
straw, its wobbly lamp set on an old crate that served as a
night table, its wicker trunk full of linen, its stool with
clothes piled up on it; and the third room, unused, that
they never went into. Then the stone stairway, the huge
entry hall perpetually menaced by sand; the street—three
two-story buildings, a shed where sponges were dried, a
vacant lot; the city around them.

They doubtless spent the oddest months of their whole
lives in Sfax.

Sfax, whose port and European quarter had been destroyed during the war, was made up of about thirty streets cutting across each other at right angles. The two main streets were the avenue Bourguiba, which went from the railroad station to the central market, near which they lived, and the avenue Hedi-Chaker, which went from the port to the Arab quarter. Their intersection formed the center of the city: located there were the city hall, whose two downstairs halls contained a few old pieces of pottery and a half-dozen mosaics; the statue and the tomb of Hedi-Chaker, assassinated by the Red Hand shortly before independence; the Café de Tunis, frequented by Arabs, and the Café de la Régence, frequented by Europeans; a little flower bed, a newspaper kiosk, a tobacco store.

One could circle the European quarter in just a little more than a quarter of an hour. The Technical High School was three minutes away from the building they lived in, the market two minutes, the restaurant where they ate all their meals five, the Café de la Régence six, as were the bank, the municipal library, and six of the seven movie theaters in town. The post office and the railroad station, and the place to rent cars for Tunis or Gabès, were less than ten minutes away, and constituted the extreme limits of what it sufficed to be acquainted with to live in Sfax.

The beautiful old fortified Arab town offered grayish-brown walls, and doors which were considered admirable, and rightly so. They often went inside the Arab town and made it almost the only destination of all their walks, but since they were really only strollers they always remained outsiders. They did not understand even its simplest mechanisms; they saw in it only a labyrinth of streets. They would look up and admire a forged iron balcony, a painted beam, the pure pointed arch of a window, a subtle play of light and shadow, an extremely narrow stairway, but their walks were aimless; they went round and round, feared at every instant that they would get lost, and tired quickly. Nothing, in the end, seemed attractive to them in this succession of miserable shops, almost identical stores, and native bazaars crowded together, in this incomprehensible alternation of swarming streets and empty streets, in this crowd that as far as they could see was going nowhere.

This sensation of being outsiders was accentuated, became almost oppressive, when with long empty afternoons before them, or dispiriting Sundays, they went all through the Arab part of the city and, beyond Bab Djebli, reached the endless suburbs of Sfax. For whole kilometers there were tiny gardens, hedges of prickly pear, mud huts, sheet-iron and cardboard shacks, then immense, deserted, putrid lagoons, and at the very end of them, the first fields of olives. They loitered about for hours; they passed by garrisons, and walked across vacant lots and muddy sections of town.

And when they came back to the European quarter, when they passed the Hillal movie theater or the Nour, when they sat down at the Régence, clapped their hands to call the waiter, ordered a Coca-Cola or a stein of beer, bought the latest *Le Monde,* whistled for the vendor, always dressed in a long dirty white smock and a canvas skullcap on his head, to buy a few cones of peanuts, toasted almonds, pistachio nuts and pine nuts from him—then they had the dreary feeling that this was home.

They would walk alongside palm trees gray with dust; they would walk along the neo-Moorish façades of the buildings along the avenue Bourguiba; they would glance vaguely at the hideous shop windows: frail furniture, iron-work candelabra, electric blankets, notebooks for school-boys, street dresses, ladies' shoes, bottles of butane gas—it was their only world, their real world. They would trudge back home. Jérôme would make coffee in coffeemakers imported from Czechoslovakia; Sylvie would correct a pile of exercises.

Jérôme had tried at first to find work. They had gone to Tunis several times, and thanks to letters of introduction he had gotten in France, and with the aid of his Tunisian friends, he had met employees in offices of the Information Service, Radio, Tourist Bureau, and National Education. It was wasted effort. Motivation studies did not exist in Tunis, nor did part-time work, and people held on to the rare soft jobs. He had no qualifications; he was neither an engineer nor an accountant nor an industrial designer nor a doctor. He was again offered jobs as a grade school teacher or assistant teacher in a high school; he didn't want them. He soon abandoned all hope. Sylvie's salary allowed them to live, frugally: this was the most usual way of living in Sfax.

Following the program for the year, Sylvie wore herself out trying to explain the hidden beauties of Malherbe and Racine to pupils taller than she was who didn't know how to write. Jérôme wasted his time. He started on different projects that he could never carry out: preparing to pass an examination in sociology, trying to put his ideas about movies into shape. He loitered in the streets in his Weston shoes, strode up and down the port, wandered through the market. He went to the museum, exchanged a few words with the guard, looked for a while at an old amphora, a tombstone inscription, a mosaic: Daniel in the lions' den,

Amphitrite riding a dolphin. He went to watch a tennis match on the courts set up at the foot of the ramparts, he crossed the Arab quarter, he loitered in the native bazaars, hefting fabrics, brass pieces, saddles. He bought all the newspapers, did the crossword puzzles, borrowed books from the library, wrote his friends rather sad letters that often were not answered.

Sylvie's schedule established the rhythm of their life. Their week was made up of lucky days—Mondays, because the morning was free and because the bill changed at the movie, Wednesdays, because the afternoon was free, Fridays, because the whole day was free and the movie programs changed again—and unlucky days: the rest of the week. Sunday was a neutral day, agreeable in the morning because they stayed in bed and the weeklies from Paris came, dragging in the afternoon, sinister in the evening, unless a movie by chance appealed to them, but it was rare for two worth-while or even tolerable films to be shown in the same half-week. And so the weeks went by. They succeeded each other with mechanical regularity: four weeks made a month, more or less, and the months were all alike. The days, after having grown shorter and shorter, became longer and longer. Winter was damp, cold almost. Their life flowed by.

THEY WERE ALL ALONE.

Sfax was an opaque town. On certain days it seemed to them that no one could ever enter into it. Its doors would never open. There were people on the streets in the evening, dense crowds coming and going, an almost continuous wave beneath the arcades of the avenue Hedi-Chaker, in front of the Hôtel Mabrouk, in front of the Centre de Propagande of the Destour, in front of the Hillal theater, in front of the Délices pastry shop. There were public places that were almost full: cafés, restaurants, movie houses; and faces which might for a moment seem familiar. But all around them, along the port, along the ramparts, as soon as one got a little way away, there was only emptiness, death: the immense sandy esplanade in front of the hideous cathedral, surrounded with dwarf palms, the boulevard de Picville, bordered with vacant lots, two-story houses; the rue Mangolte, the rue Fezzani, the rue Abd-el-Kader Zghal, naked and deserted, dark and rectilinear, swept with sand. The wind shook the rickety palms: trunks swollen with woody scales, from which there barely emerged a few palm leaves in a fan. Multitudes of cats crept into garbage cans. A dog with yellow hair passed by from time to time, sticking close to the walls, its tail between its legs.

Not a soul around: behind the doors that were always closed, nothing but bare corridors, stone stairways, blind courtyards. Street after street going off at right angles, iron curtains, palings, a world of false plazas, false streets, phantom avenues. They would walk silently along, disoriented, and sometimes they had the impression that Sfax did not exist, did not breathe. They looked about them for signs of secret sympathy. There was no answer. It was an almost painful sensation of isolation. They were dispossessed of this world, they did not feel at home in it; it did not belong to them and never would belong to them. It was as if a very ancient order had been given, once and for all, a strict rule that excluded them: they would be allowed to go where they pleased, they would not be bothered, no one would say a word to them. They would remain unknown, strangers. The Italians, the Maltese, the Greeks of the port would silently watch them go by; the great olive-growers, all dressed in white, with their glasses with gold frames, walking slowly down the rue du Bey followed by their bodyguards, would pass them by without seeing them.

They had only passing, and often distant, relations with Sylvie's colleagues. The French teachers who had tenure didn't seem very impressed with those who had come under contract. Even those not bothered by this distinction found it more difficult to forgive Sylvie for not being what they would have liked her to be: the wife of a professor and herself a professor, a good provincial petite bourgeoise, dignified, reserved, cultured. They represented France. Yet somehow there were still two Frances—that of beginning professors who wanted to acquire a little house in Angoulême, Béziers, or Tarbes as soon as they could, and that of the refractory or rebellious who did not get the extra one-third of their salary for colonial service but could allow themselves to scorn the others—but this latter was a species on the way to becoming extinct, for most of them had been pardoned and others were leaving for jobs in Algeria, in Guinea. But neither of the two sorts seemed ready to admit that one might sit in the first row in movie houses alongside the raft of native kids, or loiter in the streets like a good-for-nothing, in old shoes, unshaven, disheveled. There were a few exchanges of books, of records, a few rare discussions at the Régence, and that was all. No warm invitation, no lively friendship—that was something that didn't thrive in Sfax. People curled up inside themselves, in their houses that were too big for them.

With the others, with the French employees of the Compagnie Sfax-Gafsa or Pétroles, with the Moslems, the Jews, the French born in Tunisia, it was still worse: contact was impossible. Sometimes they didn't speak to a soul for a whole week.

It soon came to seem as if life had stopped. Time passed, motionless. They no longer had any link with the world, except for newspapers that were always too old and for all they knew might even be nothing but pious lies, memories of a former life, reflections of another world. They had always lived in Sfax and would always live there. They had no more plans, were no longer impatient. They looked forward to nothing, not even to vacations that were always too far away, not even to returning to France.

They experienced neither joy nor sadness, nor even boredom, but they sometimes asked themselves whether they were still alive, whether they were really alive. They got no particular satisfaction from this misleading question, except for one elusive thing: it sometimes seemed to them, dimly, obscurely, that this life was adequate, what it should be, and, paradoxically, necessary. They were at the heart of a void, they were settled down in a no man's land of straight streets, yellow sand, lagoons, gray palm trees, in a world they didn't understand, that they didn't try to understand. For never in their past life had they been prepared to have to adapt themselves someday, transform themselves, model themselves on a landscape, a climate, a way of life. Sylvie did not for an instant resemble the professor she was supposed to be, and Jérôme could give the impression, as he loitered in the streets, that he had brought his country, or rather his neighborhood, his ghetto, his section of town along with him beneath the soles of his English shoes. But the rue Larbi-Zarouk, where they had chosen to live, did not even have the mosque that is the glory of the rue de Quatrefages, and as for the rest, no matter how hard they sometimes tried to imagine them, there was no boulevard Mac-Mahon, no Harry's Bar, no Balzar, no Contrescarpe, no Salle Pleyel, no banks of the Seine on a June night. But in this void, precisely because of this void, because of this absence of everything, this fundamental emptiness, this neutral zone, this clean slate, it seemed to them that they were becoming purified, that they were rediscovering a greater simplicity, a true modesty. And, certainly, in the general poverty of Tunisia, their own misery, their mild discomfort as civilized individuals used to showers, cars, iced drinks, no longer had much sense.

Sylvie taught her classes, asked her pupils questions, corrected their homework. Jérôme went to the municipal library, read books at random: Borges, Troyat, Zeraffa. They ate their meals in a little restaurant, at the same table almost every day, the same meal almost every day: tuna salad, breaded cutlet or shish-kebab or fried sole, and fruit. They would go to the Régence to have an espresso and the glass of cold water that came with it. They read piles of newspapers, saw movies, loitered in the streets.

Their life was like a habit they had had too long, like an almost peaceful boredom: a life that had nothing.

FROM APRIL ON THEY TOOK A FEW TRIPS. Sometimes when they had three or four days free and were not too short of money, they would rent a car and go south. Or else on Saturday at six in the evening a jitney taxi would take them to Sousse or Tunis till Monday at noon.

They tried to get away from Sfax, its dismal streets, its emptiness, and find in panoramic views, in horizons, in ruins something that would dazzle them, overwhelm them, warm splendors that would avenge them. The ruins of a palace, a temple, a theater, a green oasis discovered from the heights of a mountaintop, a long beach of fine sand stretching in a semicircle from one end of the horizon to the other sometimes rewarded them for having sought them out. But usually they left Sfax only to come across—a few dozen or a few hundred kilometers farther on—the same dismal streets, the same teeming and incomprehensible bazaars, the same lagoons, the same ugly palm trees, the same aridity.

They saw Gabès, Tozeur, Nefta, Gafsa and Metlaoui, the ruins of Sbeitla, Kasserine, Thélepte. They went through dead cities whose names had once seemed magic: Maharès, Moularès, Matmata, Médénine. They pushed on as far as the Libyan border.

For kilometer after kilometer it was a stony, gray, uninhabitable land. Nothing grew there except thin tufts of almost yellow grass with sharp-pointed blades. It seemed to them that they traveled for hours in a cloud of dust along a road marked only by old ruts, or the half-erased tracks of tires, with no other horizons than soft grayish hills, coming across nothing except, on occasion, the carcass of a donkey, an old rusty tin oil drum, a pile of stones half caved in that perhaps once had been a house.

Or else along a road that was well marked but cut up and here and there almost dangerous, they would cross immense salt deposits, and on each side, as far as the eye could see, there would be a white crust that shone in the sunlight, causing flickering shimmerings on the horizon that now and then almost resembled mirages, waves breaking, crenelated walls. They would stop the car and walk a few steps. Under the crust of salt, light brown stretches of dry cracked clay sometimes gave way, leaving darker zones of compact, rubbery mud that their feet might almost sink into.

Camels with their hair peeling off, their feet entangled in their tethers, biting off leaves of a curiously twisted tree with great movements of their heads, turning their stupid thick lips toward the highway, mangy, half-wild dogs running round and round, crumbling walls of dry stones, goats with long black hair, low tents made out of patched blankets announced villages and towns: a long succession of square, one-story houses, dirty-white façades, the square tower of a minaret, the dome of a little mosque. They passed a peasant trotting along beside his donkey, and stopped at the only hotel.

Three men squatting at the foot of a wall were eating bread that they moistened in a little oil. Children were running about. A woman, completely draped in a black or purple veil that covered even her eyes, sometimes glided from one house to another. The terraces of the two cafés overflowed into the street. A loud-speaker broadcasted Arab music: strident modulations, taken up over and over again, repeated in chorus, litanies of a piercing flute, the rasping sound of tambourines and zithers. Men sitting around in the shade were drinking little glasses of tea, playing dominoes.

They passed enormous cisterns, and reached the ruins by a difficult path: four columns seven yards high, which no longer held up anything, houses fallen to pieces though their ground plan was still intact, with the square trace of each room marked on the ground, uneven steps, cellars, paved streets, remains of sewers. And so-called guides offered them little silver fish, pieces with a patina, little statuettes in terra cotta.

Then, before they left, they entered the markets, the bazaars. They got lost in the labyrinth of galleries, blind alleys, passages. A barber was shaving customers in the open air, next to an enormous pile of porous bowls. A donkey was laden with two conical baskets of plaited rope, filled with powdered peppers. In the goldsmiths' market, in the fabric market, barefoot merchants sitting cross-legged on piles of blankets unrolled rugs of thick wool and clipped wool for them, offered them burnooses in red wool, veils in wool or silk, leather saddles decorated in silver, hammered copper plates, carved wood, firearms, musical instruments, little jewels, shawls embroidered in gold, parchments decorated with great arabesques.

They bought nothing, in part, doubtless, because they did not know how to buy and felt uneasy about having to bargain, but above all because they didn't feel attracted. None of these objects, however sumptuous they sometimes were, gave them an impression of richness. They passed by, amused or indifferent, but everything they saw remained

Georges Perec

foreign to them, belonged to another world, didn't concern them. And they brought back from these trips only images of emptiness, of dryness: desolate brush, steppes, lagoons, a mineral world where nothing could grow, the world of their own loneliness, their own aridity.

Yet it was in Tunis that they one day saw their dream house, the loveliest of places to live. It was at Hammamet, the home of an aging English couple who divided their time between Tunisia and Florence, for whom hospitality seemed to have become the only way not to die of the boredom of each other's company. There were a good dozen other guests besides Jérôme and Sylvie. The things going on were pointless and even exasperating: little party games, bridge games, canasta games alternated with rather snobbish conversations in which fairly recent gossip straight from the capitals of the West led to knowing and often trenchant remarks ("I like the man very much and what he's doing is fine . . .").

But the house was heaven on earth. In the center of a great park that sloped gently toward a beach with fine sand, an old building in the local style, quite small, with no upper floors, had developed from year to year, had finally become the sun of a constellation of pavilions in all sizes and all styles, gloriettes, little mosques, bungalows, surrounded by verandas, scattered all about the park and linked by galleries with skylights. There was an octagonal room, with no other openings but a little door and two narrow peepholes, with thick walls entirely lined with books, as dark and cool as a tomb. There were tiny rooms, whitewashed like monks' cells, with two Sahara armchairs and a low table as the only furniture, and other long, low, narrow rooms with thick mats, and still others

114

furnished in the English style with window seats and monumental fireplaces flanked by two divans facing each other. In the garden, paths of white marble bordered by antique statuary and fragments of columns wound among the lemon trees, the orange trees, the almond trees. There were brooks and waterfalls, rock grottoes, basins covered with great white water lilies among which from time to time there streaked the silvery trace of fish. Peacocks strutted about freely, as they did in their dreams. Arcades smothered in roses led to nests of greenery.

But it was, doubtless, too late. The three days they spent at Hammamet did not shake off their lethargy. It seemed to them that this luxury, this ease, this profusion of offerings, this immediate evidence of beauty no longer concerned them. They would once have damned themselves for the painted tiles of the bathrooms, for the fountains of the gardens, for the Scotch carpet in the great entry hall, for the oak paneling in the library, for the porcelains, for the vases, for the rugs. They hailed them as a memory; they had not become insensitive to them, but they no longer understood them; they lacked points of reference. It was doubtless in this Tunis, in this cosmopolitan Tunis with traces of prestige, a pleasant climate, a picturesque and highly colorful life, that they could most easily have settled down. It was, doubtless, this life that they had once dreamed of: but they had become nothing but inhabitants of Sfax, provincials, exiles.

A world without recollections, without memory. Time still went by, desert-like days and weeks which did not count. They no longer hankered after anything. An indifferent world. Trains came in, boats anchored in port, unloaded machine tools, medicine, ball bearings, took on phosphates, oil. Trucks loaded with straw crossed the city, went south where there was famine. Their life went on exactly the same as usual: hours teaching, espressos at the Régence, old films in the evening, newspapers, crossword puzzles. They were sleepwalkers. They no longer knew what they wanted. They were dispossessed persons.

It now seemed to them that before—and this "before" each day became farther back in time, as if their previous history was slipping into legend, into the unreal or the formless—before, they had at least had a furious desire to possess. This need had often taken the place of living. They had felt keyed up, impatient, devoured with desires.

And then what? What had they done? What had happened?

Something that resembled a very mild, very quiet tragedy had settled down at the heart of their slow-motion life. They were lost in the ruins of a very old dream, in formless debris.

Nothing was left. They were at the end of the road, at the end of this ambiguous trajectory that had been their life for six years, at the end of this vague quest that had led them nowhere, that had taught them nothing.

# Epilogue

T HEY COULD HAVE GONE ON LIKE THAT. They could have
stayed there the rest of their lives. Jérôme would have
gotten a job too. They would not have lacked for money.
They would eventually have been appointed to posts in
Tunis. They would have made new friends. They would
have bought a car. They would have had a fine villa, a
large garden at la Marsa, at Sidi bou Saîd, at el Manza.

But it will not be so easy for them to escape their history.
Time, once again, will work in their place. The school
year will end. The warm weather will be delightful.
Jérôme will spend his days at the beach, and Sylvie, once
her classes are over, will join him there. The last com-
positions will be handed in. They will feel vacation time
coming on. They will feel nostalgic about Paris, the banks
of the Seine in spring, their tree bursting into flower, the
Champs-Élysées, the Place des Vosges. They will be moved
by the memory of the freedom they cherished so, their
lazy mornings, their meals by candlelight. Friends will
send along plans for a vacation: a big house in Touraine,
good food, picnics in the countryside.
"How about going back?" one of them will say.
"Everything could be the same as it was before," the
other will say.

They will pack their bags. They will put away books,
engravings, photographs of their best friends, throw away

119

innumerable papers, give away their furniture, their poorly carpentered bookshelves, their perforated bricks, send off their trunks. They will count the days, the hours, the minutes.

For their last hours in Sfax they will gravely take their ritual walk. They will go through the central market, go along the port for a minute, admire, as they do every day, the enormous sponges drying in the sun, pass by the Italian sausage store, the Hôtel des Oliviers, the municipal library, then, coming back along the avenue Bourguiba, go along the hideous cathedral, cut off in front of the school where they will say hello for the last time, as they do every day, to Monsieur Michri, the guard pacing up and down in front of the entrance, take the rue Victor-Hugo, go by their familiar restaurant in front of the Greek church. Then they will enter the Arab quarter by the Porte de la Kasbah, take the rue Bab Djedid, then the rue du Fey, come out by the Porte Bab Diwan, reach the arcades of the avenue Hedi-Chaker, go past the theater, the two movie houses, the bank, drink a last cup of coffee at the Régence, buy their last cigarettes, their last newspapers.

Two minutes later they will take their places in a rented Peugeot 403 all ready to leave. Their suitcases will long since have been tied to the roof. They will press to their hearts their money, their boat and train tickets, their baggage checks.

The car will take off slowly. At 5:30 in the evening, at the beginning of summer, Sfax will be a really beautiful city. Its immaculate buildings will shine in the sun. The towers and crenelated walls of the Arab town will look splendid. Boy Scouts all dressed in red and white will march by in step. Great red flags with the white crescent of

Tunisia, with the red and green of Algeria, will float in the light breeze.

There will be a stretch of sea, all blue, great buildings under construction, endless suburbs crowded with donkeys, children, bicycles, then endless groves of olives. Then the road: Sakiet-es-Zit, el Djem and its amphitheater, Msaken, the city of thieves, Sousse and its overpopulated sea front, Enfidaville and its immense olive groves, Bir bou Rebka and its cafés, its fruit, its potters' shops, Grombalia, Potinville with its vines invading the hills, Hammam Lif, then a stretch of highway, industrial suburbs, soap factories, cement factories: Tunis.

They will take a long swim at Carthage, amid ruins, and at la Marsa; they will go to Utique, Kelibia, Nabeul, where they will buy pottery, to la Goulette, where late at night they will eat the unusual giltheads.

Then one morning at six o'clock they will be at the port. Getting aboard will be a long and tiring process; they will have trouble finding a place on deck to put their deck chairs.

The crossing will be uneventful. They will drink a café au lait with croissants in Marseille. They will buy a copy of *Le Monde* of the night before, and *Libération*. In the train the noise of the wheels will set up the rhythms of songs of victory, the Hallelujah Chorus from *The Messiah,* triumphal hymns. They will count the kilometers; they will be ecstatic when they see the French countryside, its great fields of wheat, its green forests, its pastures and its valleys.

They will arrive at eleven o'clock at night. All their friends will be waiting for them. They will exclaim over how well they look; they will be tanned like great travelers, and will be wearing big woven straw hats. They will tell all about Sfax, the desert, the magnificent ruins, how inexpensive it is to live there, the bright blue sea. They will be taken to Harry's Bar. They will immediately get drunk. They will be happy.

They will be back, and things will be worse. They will go back to the rue de Quatrefages, its tree that is so pretty, the little apartment that is so charming with its low ceiling, its window with red curtains and its window with green curtains, its nice old books, its piles of newspapers, its narrow bed, its tiny kitchen, its untidiness.

They will see Paris again, and it will be a real celebration. They will loiter along the Seine, in the gardens of the Palais Royal, in the little streets of Saint-Germain. And each night in the lighted streets each shop window will be a marvelous invitation. Stalls will totter beneath the weight of food. They will press through the crowds in the big department stores. They will plunge their hands into the piles of silks, caress the heavy flacons of perfume, touch the ties.

They will try to live as they did before. They will renew relations with the same agencies as before. But the charm will be broken. They will feel stifled again. They will think they are dying of niggardliness, scantiness.

They will dream of a fortune. They will look in gutters in the hope of finding a fat wallet, a bank note, a hundred-franc piece, a subway ticket.

They will dream of fleeing to the country. They will dream of Sfax.

Then one day—hadn't they always known that this day would come?—they will decide to end this sort of life, once and for all, like everybody else. Their friends, put on the alert, will look for work for them. They will be recommended at several agencies. They will hopefully write careful résumés. Chance—but not exactly chance—will be on their side. In spite of its irregularity their experience will receive particular attention. They will be called for an interview. They will find the right words to make a good impression.

Thus after a few years of gypsy life, tired of being short of money, tired of counting pennies and being angry at themselves for counting them, Jérôme and Sylvie will accept, with gratitude perhaps, responsible jobs for both of them, along with a salary that might even be considered a real windfall, offered them by a big wheel in advertising.

They will go to Bordeaux to take over an agency. They will make careful preparations for their departure. They will put their apartment in order, have it repainted, get rid of the heaps of books, the bundles of clothes, the piles of dishes that had always made it seem crowded and had often seemed about to stifle them. And almost without recognizing it, they will wander through this two-room apartment that they had so often said was impossible in every way, and impossible first of all to wander through. For the first time they will see it as they had always dreamed of seeing it, repainted finally, sparkling white, sparkling clean, without a single speck of dust, spotless, no cracks, no torn places, with its low ceiling, its country courtyard, its wonderful tree that soon future renters will grow ecstatic about, as they once did.

They will sell their books to second-hand booksellers, their old clothes to second-hand dealers. They will run to tailors, dressmakers, haberdashers. They will pack their trunks.

They will not earn a fortune. They will not be presi-

dents or sit on a board of directors. They will handle only
other people's millions. They will be left a few crumbs,
for prestige, for smoke-tanned peccary gloves. They will
make a good impression. They will be well-housed, well-
fed, well-dressed. They will have nothing to regret.

They will have the Chesterfield divan, their armchairs
of natural leather as supple and smart as Italian car seats,
their rustic tables, their lecterns, their rugs, their silk car-
pets, their library shelves in light oak.

They will have immense, well-lighted empty rooms,
spacious arrangements, glass walls, private views. They will
have porcelains, silver table services, lace napkins, rich red
leather bookbindings.

They will not yet be thirty. They will have a whole
life ahead of them.

They will leave Paris one September at the beginning
of the month. They will have a first-class railway car almost all to themselves. The train will pick up speed almost
immediately. The aluminum coach will sway gently back
and forth.

They will leave. They will abandon everything. They
will flee. Nothing will have been able to hold them back.

"Remember?" Jérôme will say. And they will remember
time gone by, somber days, their youth, the times they
first met, the tree in the court of the rue de Quatrefages,
friends that have disappeared, fraternal meals. They will
see themselves crossing Paris in search of cigarettes, stopping in front of antique dealers' windows. They will relive
the old days in Sfax, their almost triumphant return.

"Well, here we are," Sylvie will say. And that will seem almost natural to them.

They will feel comfortable in their light clothes. They will lounge about in the empty compartment. The French countryside will glide by. They will look in silence at the great fields of ripe wheat, the bare wires of the high-tension poles. They will see flour mills, factories that look almost elegant, great vacation camps, dams, little isolated houses in the middle of clearings. Children will run along a white road.

For a long time the trip will be pleasant. At noon or thereabouts they will nonchalantly make their way toward the dining car. They will sit down next to a window, just the two of them alone. They will order two whiskies. They will look at each other, one last time, with the smile of accomplices. The starched linen, the heavy silver table service marked with the arms of the Wagons-Lits, the thick plates with a coat of arms, will seem the prelude to a sumptuous feast. But the meal they are served will be really tasteless.

*The means are part of the truth, as well as the result. The search for truth must itself be true; true research is truth spread out before us, the scattered members of which are reunited in the result.*

—KARL MARX